## Dedication

Dedicated to Warren Cresswell (1962 – 2009), who was conference organiser for The Mamm
Symposium *Advances in Ecological Impact Assessment for Mammals* in November 2007 an
informal gathering of mammalogists in November 2009, from which this publication arose.

## Authors and Editors

Johnny Birks BSc, PhD, MIEEM
*Swift Ecology*

Simone Bullion BSc, PhD, MIEEM
*Suffolk Wildlife Trust*

Warren Cresswell BSc, PhD, CEnv, MIEEM, MIoD

Mike Dean BSc, MSc, CEnv, MIEEM
*MD Ecology Ltd*

John Gurnell BSc, PhD
*Queen Mary, London University*

Andrew C. Kitchener BSc, PhD, FRZSS
*National Museums Scotland*

Peter Lurz BSc, PhD
*Edinburgh*

Pat Morris BSc, PhD
*Royal Holloway, University of London (retired)*

Marina Pacheco BSc, MSc
*The Mammal Society*

Will Trewhella BA, MSc, PhD, MIEEM
*Cresswell (a Hyder Consulting group company)*

David Wells BSc, CEnv, MIEEM
*David Wells Ecology*

Phil Wheeler BA, PhD
*University of Hull*

Stephanie Wray BSc, PhD, MBA, CEnv, FIEEM
*Biocensus*

Derek Yalden BSc, PhD
*University of Manchester (retired)*

Linda Yost BSc, MSc, CEnv, MIEEM
*Institute of Ecology and Environmental
Management*

**Red squirrel.**
[Peter Lurz].

i

# Foreword and Acknowledgements

Some UK BAP mammals, such as dormice and water voles, have conservation handbooks that provide guidelines on, for example, their ecology, suitable survey methodologies, legal protection, impact assessment and mitigation. However, tor others, particularly those added recently to the UK BAP list, this is not the case. This was highlighted in a review paper by Jo Treweek at The Mammal Society's autumn symposium *Advances in Ecological Impact Assessment for Mammals in 2007*; mammals, in particular UK BAP species that were not otherwise protected, were not receiving adequate attention in terms of Ecological Impact Assessment (EclA).

As a follow on from this symposium, the late Warren Cresswell (one of the symposium co-organisers) and The Mammal Society organised an informal workshop in early November 2009, with attendees discussing (with apologies to Donald Rumsfeld), the known knowns (the things we know), the known unknowns (the things we do not know) and the unknown unknowns (the things we do not know we don't know) concerning several UK BAP mammals, particularly with reference to the impacts on these species from development projects. The workshop identified significant knowledge gaps for some species, and it was agreed that it would be beneficial to produce a publication offering guidance, written by species experts, to assist people undertaking EclAs. The species in question were the red squirrel, harvest mouse, brown and mountain hare, European hedgehog, wildcat, pine marten and polecat. Shortly after the gathering in November 2009, Warren passed away at far too young an age. He would have greatly enjoyed putting together this publication, and his depth and breadth of knowledge and sheer enthusiasm, would have, no doubt, greatly speeded up its production. The editors and authors hope he would have approved of this finished article.

This publication recognises that there is a need for further scientific research on aspects of ecology and survey methodology for some or all of the species considered here, a need to develop further some mitigation strategies, and a need to collate and analyse examples of ongoing mitigation strategies (both successful and unsuccessful); hence, the 'interim' nature of the title. The editors actively seek feedback and case studies that could be used to update this publication in the future; please see the Mammal Society web site http://www.mammal.org.uk/bap-interim-guidance-updates.

The editors would like to thank Linda Yost at the Institute of Ecology and Environmental Management, Liz Halliwell and Jean Matthews at the Countryside Council for Wales, Kat Walsh at Natural England, Jenny Bryce and Rob Raynor at Scottish Natural Heritage, for their invaluable comments and feedback on earlier drafts of this publication.

The editors would like to thank the following organisations for their support for this publication: Belos Ecology; The Cambrian Ecological Partnership; Conservation Construction Ltd; Cresswell (a Hyder Consulting group company); the Institute of Ecolofgy and Environmental Management; national Grid; and RSK.

The editors would like to thank all the photographers who gave permission for use of their images in this publication.

This publication is endorsed by The Mammal Society, the Institute of Ecology and Environmental Management, the Countryside Council for Wales, Natural England and Scottish Natural Heritage.

The information in this book is believed to be accurate and up-to-date but the authors, editors, The Mammal Society and Hyder Consulting (UK) Limited accept no liability for any loss whatsoever (whether direct, indirect or consequential) that may be suffered through use of, or reliance on, this material by any party.

May 2012

**Pine marten.**
[Frank Greenaway/
The Vincent Wildlife Trust].

# Contents

# Contents

## List of Figures

# Contents

## List of Tables

# 1. Introduction

*By W. J. Cresswell, W. J. Trewhella, D. Wells and L. Yost*

## 1.1. Background

Following the review of United Kingdom Biodiversity Action Plan (UK BAP) species, 18 terrestrial mammals were listed as Priority Species (Biodiversity Reporting and Information Group 2007). The presence of any of these UK BAP species should be taken into account where an Environmental Impact Assessment (EIA) is required. The EIA directive (Directive 85/337/EEC, as amended: http://ec.europa.eu/environment/eia/eia-legalcontext.htm) requires an assessment to be carried out of the 'direct, indirect, secondary and cumulative, short, medium and long-term, permanent and temporary, positive and negative effects' on biodiversity of certain plans or projects.

Decision-makers require information about the likely significant ecological effects associated with a project proposal. For the ecological component of the EIA process, the Institute of Ecology and Environmental Management's (IEEM) *Guidelines for Ecological Impact Assessment (EcIA) in the United Kingdom* (IEEM 2006) provide an evaluation tool, which sets out a standard procedure for the assessment and evaluation of those significant effects on biodiversity. These guidelines were under review at the time of this publication.[1]

EcIA can be used to support a range of environmental assessments and/or appraisals, including those for which formal EIAs are not required. It is an effective, systematic, repeatable process applicable to a wide range of situations. The Strategic Environmental Assessment (SEA) Directive refers to 'plans and programmes' (http://ec.europa.eu/environment/eia/sea-legalcontext.htm); the EIA Directive refers to 'public and private projects'; Natura 2000 refers to 'plans and projects' (http://www.natura.org). This document uses the term 'project' to cover all types of development proposal for which EcIA might be used, whether or not this forms part of a formal EIA.

A review of Environmental Statements (ESs) produced for UK development proposals in 2007 (Treweek *et al*. 2007) suggested that mammals were not receiving adequate attention in terms of EcIA, and that the information needed to evaluate impacts on population status or habitat integrity, and to recommend appropriate mitigation, was generally lacking. Although certain protected species, for example bats, water vole, otter and

dormouse were often adequately addressed in those ESs reviewed, others were not, particularly those for which published survey or mitigation guidance did not exist.

A workshop in November 2009, convened jointly by Cresswell (a Hyder Consulting Group company) and The Mammal Society, discussed survey protocols, impact assessment and mitigation, in the context of EcIA, for terrestrial UK BAP mammals for which there was not already published guidance; most of these were species added to the Priority Species list in 2007. The workshop identified significant knowledge gaps for several species, and it was agreed that it would be beneficial to produce interim guidance to assist those undertaking EcIAs for proposals that could affect UK BAP mammal species. This publication is therefore intended to provide guidance on the background biology, habitat requirements, survey methodologies, legal protection, impact assessment and mitigation/compensation measures for UK BAP mammal species for which such guidance has not already been published. Adherence to the guidance and advice offered within this publication should help to maintain and enhance the conservation status of the UK BAP mammal species, at least in the context of impacts of development projects on these species.

## 1.2. Scope of this Publication

This publication is aimed at promoting best practice among ecological consultants, and guiding appropriate decision-makers associated with a project proposal, where any form of ecological assessment is undertaken (irrespective of whether a formal EIA is required). A brief outline of the EcIA process is included to place this guidance in context.

This publication concentrates on the following eight species: red squirrel *Sciurus vulgaris*, harvest mouse *Micromys minutus*, brown hare *Lepus europaeus*, mountain hare *Lepus timidus*, hedgehog *Erinaceus europaeus*, wildcat *Felis silvestris*, pine marten *Martes martes*, and polecat *Mustela putorius*. As comprehensive guidance already exists for other UK BAP mammals, namely the hazel dormouse *Muscardinus avellanarius*, water vole *Arvicola amphibius* formerly called *A. terrestris*, seven bat species (see **Table 1.1**), and otter *Lutra lutra*, this publication provides only a brief summary of existing sources of relevant information for these species (see Chapter 9). In addition, this publication does not deal with marine mammals, of which the common seal

---

[1] See IEEM's website for news on the revised guidelines (http://www.ieem.org.uk/ecia/).

**Table 1.1.** UK BAP mammals (excluding marine species).
Those shaded in are excluded from the scope of this publication.

| Common name | Scientific name | UK BAP status | Population trend | | Comments |
|---|---|---|---|---|---|
| | | | TMP [a] 10 year trend | UK BAP trend | |
| Red squirrel | *Sciurus vulgaris* Linnaeus, 1758 | Original list | Decline | Declining | |
| Hazel dormouse | *Muscardinus avellanarius* Linnaeus, 1758 | Original list | | Declining slowly | |
| Water vole | *Arvicola amphibius* formerly *A. terrestris* Linnaeus, 1758 | Original list | Decline | Fluctuating – probably declining | |
| Harvest mouse | *Micromys minutus* Pallas, 1771 | New 2007 | | Decline | |
| Brown hare | *Lepus europaeus* Pallas, 1778 | Original list | No change | Increasing | |
| Mountain hare | *Lepus timidus* Linnaeus, 1758 | New 2007 | Decline | Declining | |
| Hedgehog | *Erinaceus europaeus* Linnaeus, 1758 | New 2007 | No change [b] | Rural decline | |
| Greater horseshoe bat | *Rhinolophus ferrumequinum* Schreber, 1774 | Original list | Increase | Increasing | |
| Lesser horseshoe bat | *Rhinolophus hipposideros* Bechstein, 1800 | Original list | Increase | Increasing | |
| Bechstein's bat | *Myotis bechsteinii* Kuhl, 1817 | Original list | | Unknown | |
| Greater mouse-eared bat | *Myotis myotis* Borkhausen, 1797 | Removed 2007 | | | Removed from the Priority Species list in 2007 as no longer thought to be present as a breeding species in the UK. |
| Noctule bat | *Nyctalus noctula* Schreber, 1774 | New 2007 | No change | Decline? | |
| Pipistrelle bat | *Pipistrellus pipistrellus* Schreber, 1774 | Superseded | | | Since publication of the original list of Key Species it has been confirmed there are two cryptic pipistrelle species, *P. pipistrellus* sens. str. and *P. pygmaeus*. Therefore pipistrelle bat, as an outdated species concept, was removed in 2007 from the Priority Species list, but soprano pipistrelle was included (see below). |
| Soprano pipistrelle | *Pipistrellus pygmaeus* Leach, 1825 | New 2007 | Stable | Fluctuating – probably stable | |
| Barbastelle bat | *Barbastella barbastellus* Schreber, 1774 | Original list | | Unknown | |
| Brown long-eared bat | *Plecotus auritus* Linnaeus, 1758 | New 2007 | Stable | Decline? | |
| Wildcat | *Felis silvestris* Schreber, 1777 | New 2007 | | Substantial decline | |
| Otter | *Lutra lutra* Linnaeus, 1758 | Original list | Increase | Increasing | |
| Pine marten | *Martes martes* Linnaeus, 1758 | New 2007 | | Unknown (N.B. apparently recovering in Scotland – see Chapter 7) | |
| Polecat | *Mustela putorius* Linnaeus, 1758 | New 2007 | No change | Slow recovery | |

[a] TMP – Tracking Mammals Partnership

[b] N.B. Data from TMP survey conflicts with section 5.3 of this publication which indicates a long-term decline.

*Phoca vitulina* and 20 cetacean species are priority species in the UK BAP, given that marine mammals will be unaffected by most land-based developments.

There is a need for further research on appropriate survey methodologies and mitigation strategies in relation to some species; for this reason this publication serves as interim guidance. It is intended that this guidance will be revised once further research has been carried out and more mitigation case studies are available.

Further justification of the need for this publication is provided by findings in the 2011 State of Britain's Mammals report (Macdonald & Burnham 2011).[2] Of the eight species considered in this publication, five have declining populations (notably wildcat, hedgehog, red squirrel, mountain hare and harvest mouse) according to Macdonald & Burnham (2011).

## 1.3. UK BAP Mammals

The UK BAP was published in 1994 (Department for the Environment 1994), as part of the UK government's commitment to biodiversity conservation following the signing of the Convention on Biological Diversity in Rio de Janeiro in 1992. The Convention called for the development and enforcement of national strategies and associated action plans to identify, conserve and protect existing biological diversity, and to enhance it wherever possible. The UK BAP describes the biological resources of the UK and provides detailed plans for conservation of these resources, at national and devolved levels. Species and Habitat Action Plans (SAPs and HAPs) were drawn up for those species and habitats considered to require targeted conservation action. Local Biodiversity Action Plans identify local priorities and determine the contribution they can make to the delivery of the national SAP/ HAP targets. From the original list of Key Species published in 1994, SAPs were developed for 11 terrestrial mammal species, including six bat species (see *Table 1.1*).

In 2005, the government commenced a priority review of the original UK BAP list, to decide on those species that should be added, removed or remain on the list. As a result, an updated list of priority species and habitats was published in August 2007. One terrestrial mammal species, the greater mouse-eared bat *Myotis myotis* was removed, as it was no longer thought to be present as a breeding species in the UK, and the soprano pipistrelle *Pipistrellus pygmaeus* was included in place of the pipistrelle bat *P. pipistrellus* agg., which was considered as one species on the original list

[2] Data from Macdonald & Burnham (2011).

of Key Species but is now known to be two. An additional nine terrestrial mammal species were added to the priority list (see *Table 1.1*). *Table 1.1* also summarises trends in populations for these species as reported by Macdonald & Burnham (2011).

Following the establishment of devolved governments in Scotland, Wales and Northern Ireland in 1998, responsibility for environmental legislation and the implementation of Biodiversity Action Plans is now at the country level. There are four Country Biodiversity Groups and each of these has published country strategies to guide their BAP work *(Biodiversity 2020: A strategy for England's wildlife and ecosystem services* (Defra 2011); Northern Ireland Action Plans http://ukbars.defra.gov.uk/plans/ni.asp; *Scotland's Biodiversity: It's in Your Hands – A strategy for the conservation and enhancement of biodiversity in Scotland* (Scottish Executive 2004); Wales Biodiversity Strategy http://ukbars.defra.gov. uk/plans/wes.asp). As of May 2011, the original UK BAP website is now presented within the Joint Nature Conservation Committee (JNCC) website, and more information on the UK BAP can be found at http://jncc.defra.gov.uk/page-5155 and the UK's Biodiversity Action Plan reporting system (BARS) site at http://ukbars.defra.gov.uk/. Because Northern Ireland shares waterways and a border with the Republic of Ireland, all-Ireland action plans have been developed for certain species so as to implement the Northern Ireland Biodiversity Strategy more effectively. These cover bats, red squirrels and the Irish hare (see: http://www. businessandbiodiversity.org/NIreland.html).

## 1.4. Policy Context for UK BAP Mammals

Separate planning policy and guidance in the UK has been produced by the devolved administrations in England, Northern Ireland, Scotland and Wales. In general, the planning implications of the presence of a UK BAP species on a development site are similar across the UK administrations, although there are differences, some of which are described below. These differences have arisen primarily because when the UK BAP was first published, it did not confer any legal or policy protection on those Key Species included. Some degree of protection has subsequently been achieved in England, Scotland and Wales through re-definition of UK BAP species as 'priority species of principal importance for biodiversity' originally through the Countryside and Rights of Way (CRoW) Act 2000 (http://www.legislation.gov. uk/ukpga/2000/37/contents) and now through the Natural Environment and Rural Communities (NERC) Act 2006 (http://www.legislation.gov. uk/ukpga/2006/16/contents) and the Nature

Conservation (Scotland) Act 2004 (http://www.legislation.gov.uk/asp/2004/6/contents).  Planning policy and guidance on species (other than legally protected species) generally relates to priority species on the lists created under these Acts, rather than the UK BAP list itself.

### England

Section 40 of the NERC Act 2006 placed a duty on all public bodies to have regard to the purpose of conserving biodiversity.  Section 41 of the same Act placed a duty on the Secretary of State to publish a list of species (and habitats) of principal importance for conserving biodiversity in England, and to take, and promote others to take, reasonably practicable steps to further their conservation.  All UK BAP mammals, except the wildcat, which is not currently present in England, are included as Priority Species on the current list.

The National Planning Policy Framework (NPPF) (Department for Communities and Local Government 2012) has recently superseded Planning Policy Statement 9 (PPS9): *Biodiversity and Geological Conservation* (ODPM 2005).  The NPPF states that planning policies should 'promote the preservation, restoration and re-creation of priority habitats, ecological networks and the protection and recovery of priority species populations, linked to national and local targets, and identify suitable indicators for monitoring biodiversity in the plan'.

At the time of writing, ODPM [3] *Circular 06/2005: Biodiversity and Geological Conservation* (ODPM 2005) is still considered valid guidance for planning authorities; where it references PPS9 it should be taken to refer to the new NPPF.

Consequently, although the NPPF does not state explicitly (as was the case in PPS9) that habitats or species listed as priorities in the UK Biodiversity Action Plan (BAP) can be a 'material consideration' in the making of planning decisions, this principle should still apply as it also appears in *Circular 06/2005*.

### Northern Ireland

A list of Priority Species for Northern Ireland was published in 2010 (NIEA 2010), updating previous published lists.  The list includes all the UK BAP mammals present in Northern Ireland, and one additional species, Nathusius' pipistrelle *Pipistrellus nathusii*, which is not on the UK Priority Species list.

Planning Policy Statement 2 on Planning and Nature Conservation (NIPS 1997) does not currently include guidance on consideration of UK BAP mammals in the planning process.

---

[3] Responsibilities that were placed in the Office of the Deputy Prime Minister have now been relocated mainly into the Department for Communities and Local Government.

### Scotland

The Nature Conservation (Scotland) Act 2004 imposed a duty on all public bodies to further the conservation of biodiversity.  The same Act also imposed a duty on Scottish ministers to publish a list of species (and habitats) considered to be of principal importance for conserving biodiversity.  This list was published in 2005 and includes all but three (hedgehog, pine marten and polecat) of the UK BAP mammal species present in Scotland, and also includes a number of other mammal species due to their legal protection, restricted distribution, decline in numbers, or because they are considered important by the Scottish public.  As a result, the Orkney vole *Microtus arvalis*, ship rat *Rattus rattus*, whiskered bat *Myotis mystacinus*, Brandt's bat *M. brandtii*, Daubenton's bat *M. daubentonii*, Natterer's bat *M. nattereri*, common pipistrelle *Pipistrellus pipistrellus* sens. str., Nathusius' pipistrelle *P. nathusii,* badger *Meles meles,* red deer *Cervus elaphus* and European roe deer *Capreolus capreolus* are included as species of principal importance in Scotland.

As public bodies, planning authorities have a legal duty to further the conservation of biodiversity by, for example, ensuring that the need to conserve biodiversity is reflected in development plans and seeking benefits for biodiversity from new developments.  However, Scottish planning policy (Scottish Planning Policy 2010) does not currently include specific guidance on consideration of UK BAP mammals in the planning process.

### Wales

In Wales, Section 40 of the NERC Act 2006 placed a duty on all public bodies to have regard to the purpose of conserving biodiversity.  Section 42 of the same Act placed a duty on the Welsh Assembly Government to publish a list of species (and habitats) of principal importance for conserving biodiversity in Wales, and to take, and promote others to take, reasonably practicable steps to further their conservation.  This updated an earlier obligation under section 74 of the CRoW Act 2000 to produce a list of species of principal importance for the conservation of biological diversity in Wales.  The list includes all the UK BAP mammal species present in Wales and also includes one mammal species, the common pipistrelle, which is not on the UK Priority Species list.

Technical Advice Note 5 on Nature Conservation and Planning (Planning Policy Wales 2009) states that 'the potential effects of a development on habitats or species listed as priorities in the UK Biodiversity Action Plan (BAP), habitats or species listed by the Assembly Government as of principal importance for the purposes of conserving biological diversity and by local biodiversity partnerships are capable of being a material consideration in the preparation of local development plans and in making planning decisions'. It is also stated that local planning authorities should further the conservation of species of principal importance through their planning function.

## 1.5. Ecological Impact Assessment (EcIA)

This publication is intended primarily to assist those undertaking the assessment of potential effects of project proposals affecting UK BAP mammal species. New project proposals should be evaluated according to established procedures, which set out an effective, systematic, repeatable process applicable to a wide range of situations. These include: changes to agricultural land and forestry; an application for a consent; to guide a development brief; or to inform a management plan.

IEEM have produced comprehensive guidelines on EcIA; a brief summary of the process and the key concepts involved are provided below.

The EcIA Guidelines (*Terrestrial, Freshwater and Coastal Environments* (IEEM 2006) and *Marine and Coastal* (IEEM 2010)) are evaluation tools; they set out a standard process to elucidate the direct and indirect effects of a project proposal on biological resources and features to decision-makers. EcIA has been defined as 'the process of identifying, quantifying and evaluating the potential impacts of defined actions on ecosystems or their components. If properly implemented it provides a scientifically defensible approach to ecosystem management' (Treweek 1999).

EcIA is an iterative process but, under the current guidelines (IEEM 2006), it should include the following stages (IEEM 2006).

(1) Scoping, involving consultation to ensure the widest possible input to the definition of the scope of an EcIA (in practice, scoping is iterative throughout the EcIA process), including:
  - identification of the likely zone(s) of influence arising from the whole lifespan of the project;
  - identification and evaluation of ecological features, resources and functions (ecological receptors) likely to be affected by the project;
  - identification of the drivers of biophysical changes attributable to the project;
  - identification of the biophysical changes likely to affect valued ecological resources and features.

(2) An assessment of whether these biophysical changes are likely to give rise to a significant ecological effect, defined as an effect on the integrity of a defined site or ecosystem and/or the conservation status of habitats or species

within a given geographical area, including cumulative effects.

(3) Refinement of the project to avoid or reduce identified negative effects and to incorporate:
  - mitigation measures;
  - compensation measures for any residual significant negative effects;
  - ecological enhancement measures to improve the wider environment;
  - an assessment of the likely efficacy and success of the proposed measures.

(4) Assessment of the ecological effects of the refined project and definition of the significance of these effects; including cumulative effects.

(5) Provision of advice on the consequences for decision making of the significant ecological effects, based on the value of the affected resource or feature.

(6) Provision for monitoring and following up the implementation and success of mitigation measures and ecological outcomes, including feedback in relation to predicted outcomes.

It is important to refer to the IEEM guidelines and glossary for interpretation and definitions of terms such as 'significance', 'mitigation', 'compensation', 'enhancement', 'scoping', 'zone of influence', 'receptor', 'importance' and 'value' in the context of EcIA. It will also be important to refer to the revised IEEM guidelines when these are published.

The end product of EcIA should be a clear statement of the ecological resources and features likely to be significantly affected: the value of these resources and features; the direct and indirect effects of the proposals; the measures proposed to avoid, mitigate or compensate for any predicted effects, monitoring proposals to ensure that mitigation/compensation measures are effective; and any proposed enhancements. Any constraints upon or limitations to the assessment should be stated and the implications of these considered.

In the context of UK BAP mammals, the lack of published guidance on survey, assessment and appropriate mitigation for some Priority Species has, until now, represented a considerable limitation to EcIAs involving project proposals where these species may occur. This interim guidance will enable UK BAP species to be considered more thoroughly in the evaluation process, despite knowledge gaps for some species. Relevant information may also be found in Newton *et al.* (2011), which provides guidance on wildlife issues for the construction industry.

## 1.6. Species Accounts

Each of the species-specific chapters provides the following information:

### Background biology

A brief summary of the background biology of the species, with particular emphasis on those aspects of a species' ecology that are relevant to survey and/or mitigation.

### Habitat requirements

A summary of the habitat requirements of the species. The species included in this publication show varying degrees of habitat specialism. Consequently, for some species presence or absence on a site can be predicted based on habitat data, but for other species this will not normally be possible.

### Status and distribution

A summary of the status and distribution of the species, based on the distribution maps published in the 4th edition of the *Mammals of the British Isles: Handbook* (Harris & Yalden 2008). If any changes in these distributions have been identified since the publication of these maps, these are identified in the text and in the map captions. The distribution covers the UK and Ireland (where appropriate), as several species have all-Ireland SAPs.

### Legislative protection

A summary of the varying levels of legal protection afforded to the species in each of the UK countries where it occurs. Original legislation should always be referred to for definitive guidance on actions which could result in wildlife offences being committed.

The relevant country licensing authorities responsible for issuing licences to permit actions that would otherwise be illegal under the relevant legislation are:

Natural England (NE) (http://www.naturalengland. org.uk/ourwork/regulation/wildlife/species/default. aspx);

The Welsh Government (http://wales.gov.uk/ topics/environmentcountryside/consmanagement/ conservationbiodiversity/wildlifelicences/?lang=en);

The Countryside Council for Wales (CCW) also issues licences for certain purposes (http://www. ccw.gov.uk/landscape--wildlife/habitats--species/ species-protection/licensing.aspx);

Scottish Natural Heritage (SNH) (http://www. snh.gov.uk/protecting-scotlands-nature/species-licensing/) [N.B. this is no longer the responsibility of the Scottish Government following the introduction of the Wildlife and Natural Environment (Scotland) Act 2011 (http://www.legislation.gov.uk/ asp/2011/6/contents/enacted)]; and

Department of the Environment (DoE) (http:// www.doeni.gov.uk/niea/biodiversity/wildlife_ management_and_licensing/).

### Summary of UK BAP Status and Recommended Actions

The recommended conservation actions (as identified by appropriate species expert groups) for each species are summarised in this section. JNCC have collated information from a variety of sources for each and every one of the 1150 species included on the UK Priority Species list (http://www.jncc.gov.uk/page-5161).

### Survey methodology

For the purposes of EcIA and development control, surveys should aim, as a minimum, to determine presence in or *probable absence* of a species from the zone of influence. Where possible and appropriate, surveys should aim to determine population size, as this may be required to allow an assessment of whether predicted effects will be significant, as well as to ensure that mitigation measures are appropriate and proportionate. However, for many of the species included in this publication there are, as yet, insufficient data comparing different survey techniques to enable confirmation that a species is probably absent from a site. Caution should be exercised in the interpretation of survey results, and where there is doubt the precautionary principle should be applied.

Surveys may be carried out to determine and document:

- presence or absence of UK BAP species that could be affected by the project;
- species distribution and abundance;
- evaluation of these resources (N.B. see IEEM guidelines on determining 'value' or 'importance');
- what mitigation might be required;
- what legal constraints apply (irrespective of the resource's value).

Each species account attempts to provide guidance on the amount of survey information that is likely to be necessary for the purposes of EcIA, and to achieve legislative compliance. For some species even presence/absence information may be difficult to achieve, and population size or density impossible to determine without extensive fieldwork more suited to a research project. Therefore, where appropriate, guidance has been provided on inferring likely presence/absence or likely importance of a site to a particular species, using habitat or off-site survey data.

The importance of carrying out a thorough desk study for any existing ecological data relating to a site/scheme and its surroundings cannot be over-emphasised. The ecological data will be obtained via requests to, or consultations with, organisations holding relevant information ranging from Statutory Nature Conservation Organisations (SNCOs) (including the MAGIC website for England http://magic.defra.gov.uk/website/magic), Local Authorities (see http://www.tagish.co.uk/tagish/links/localgov.htm), Wildlife Trusts (http://www.wildlifetrusts.org/index.php?section=localtrusts), local Biological Records Centres (http://www.nfbr.org.uk/nfbr.php), and the National Biodiversity Network's Gateway (http://data.nbn.org.uk/) (N.B. see NBN terms and conditions as data from the NBN gateway are not freely available for commercial use) to local or national specialist groups (such as The Vincent Wildlife Trust's work on polecat and pine marten distribution).

Field surveys may not always be appropriate. The decision on whether or not to survey must be made on a case-by-case basis as part of the EcIA scoping process. It should include consideration of:

- whether the species is likely to be significantly affected; and

- whether it is likely that surveys will generate meaningful data that inform the assessment of effects.

In their *Technical Guidance Series* IEEM have published '*Guidance on Preliminary Ecological Appraisal*' (IEEM 2012). Further advice on planning and designing ecological survey methods, and survey methodologies for specific taxonomic groups (including mammals), is available in Hill *et al.* (2005) and from the IEEM Sources of Survey Methods web pages (http://www.ieem.net/surveymethods.asp). It is important that surveys are carried out by competent and appropriately trained ecologists. IEEM provides guidance that sets out criteria for the knowledge, skills and experience required by ecologists undertaking a range of species survey work in a professional capacity; this covers all the species considered in this publication, with the exception of harvest mice (http://www.ieem.net/competencies.asp).

Ownership of the areas to be surveyed needs to be ascertained and permission sought, and adequate risk assessments carried out; for further information, see IEEM's *Professional Guidance Series* (IEEM 2011a; 2011b).

### Impact assessment, mitigation, compensation and enhancement

Impact assessment considers the way in which an ecological resource is affected by a project. An ecologically significant effect is defined (IEEM 2006) as an impact (negative or positive) on the integrity of a site or ecosystem and/or the conservation status of habitats or species. Thus, it is not enough simply to determine whether or not a particular UK BAP species is present on a site where change is proposed; it is necessary to understand how that

species and its conservation status are likely to be affected. Unfortunately, for several of the species in this publication, there is a lack of information on how individuals or populations are likely to respond to the activities associated with development projects. Again, it may be necessary to take a precautionary approach when predicting the significance of effects.

Because the amount of information available on assessing effects and addressing these through mitigation varies considerably between species in this publication, this section also varies in the amount of detail that can be provided. Guidance is provided for different types of impact, such as habitat loss, habitat fragmentation, mortality of animals, disturbance, and other species-specific impacts where appropriate. Guidance is also provided on the geographical frame of reference for determining the importance of the given ecological resource, along the following levels – International > UK > National > Regional > County > District > Local or Parish, following the IEEM guidelines.

Mitigation involves measures taken to avoid or reduce negative effects. Compensation involves measures taken to off-set the loss of, or permanent damage to, biological resources despite mitigation. However, there is little information available, as yet, on the success of mitigation and compensation measures for some of these species. Therefore it will be particularly important to consider how a species is likely to respond, not just to the activities associated with the project, but also to mitigation and compensation measures, and to ensure that the mitigation package proposed is both proportionate yet precautionary.

Monitoring the success of mitigation and compensation measures will also be critical for refining and improving them in future. There is a wealth of experience in mitigation for some of the mammal species listed in the UK BAP, such as ledges and tunnels beneath road schemes for otters, artificial roost sites for bats, and habitat management in areas supporting water voles. In respect of the other mammals covered here, it is hoped that this guidance will provide sufficient detail for mitigation and compensation measures to be used more often, and more widely, and for a similar body of experience on the likely success of mitigation measures to develop as a result.

Enhancement involves a new benefit to biodiversity, unrelated to any negative impact. Opportunities for enhancement should be sought where possible, particularly if these help to deliver relevant UK BAP or other policy objectives.

### Research recommendations

This publication is specifically termed 'Interim Guidance' as it is recognised that there will be key issues for each species (for instance on biology/ ecology, effective survey methodologies, methods of impact assessment and case studies on successful mitigation) that need further research, so as to improve this guidance in a later publication. The editors welcome feedback on relevant research, along with case studies of mitigation in practice.

## 1.7. References

Biodiversity Reporting and Information Group (2007) *Report on the Species and Habitat Review*. Report to the UK Biodiversity Partnership.

Department for Communities and Local Government (2012) *National Planning Policy Framework*. http://www.communities.gov.uk/ publications/planningandbuilding/nppf

Department for the Environment (1994) *Biodiversity: the UK Action Plan*. HMSO.

Defra (2011) *Biodiversity 2020: A strategy for England's wildlife and ecosystem services*. Defra. http://www.defra.gov.uk/publications/files/ pb13583-biodiversity-strategy-2020-111111.pdf

Harris, S. & Yalden, D.W. (2008) *Mammals of the British Isles: Handbook,* 4th edition. The Mammal Society.

Hill, D., Fasham, M., Tucker, P., Shewry, M. and Shaw, P. (eds) (2005) *Handbook of Biodiversity Methods: Survey, Evaluation and Monitoring*. Cambridge University Press.

IEEM (2006) *Guidelines for Ecological Impact Assessment in the United Kingdom: Terrestrial, Freshwater and Coastal Environments*. (version 7 July 2006). http://www.ieem.org.uk/ecia/index.html

IEEM (2010) *Guidelines for Ecological Impact Assessment in Britain and Ireland: Marine and Coastal*. http://www.ieem.net/marine-ecia/

IEEM (2011a) *Professional Guidance Series No. 5: Access to Land*. http://www.ieem.net/guidance.asp

IEEM (2011b) *Professional Guidance Series No. 8: Risk Assessment for Lone Workers*. http://www.ieem.net/guidance.asp

IEEM (2012) *Technical Guidance Series. Guidance on Preliminary Ecological Appraisal*. http://www.ieem.net/gpea.asp

Macdonald, D. W. & Burnham, D. (2011) *The State of Britain's Mammals 2011*. People's Trust for Endangered Species.

Newton, J., Nicholson, B. & Saunders, R. (2011) *Working with Wildlife: Guidance for the Construction Industry*. CIRIA, London.

NIEA (2010) *Northern Ireland Priority Species List*. http://www.ni-environment.gov.uk/northern_ ireland_priority_species_list.pdf

NIPS (1997) *PPS 2 Planning and Nature Conservation*. Northern Ireland Planning Service.

ODPM (2005a) *PPS 9: Biodiversity and Geological Conservation*. Published for the Office of the Deputy Prime Minster by The Stationery Office.

ODPM (2005b) *Circular 06/05: Biodiversity and Geological Conservation – Statutory Obligations and Their Impact Within the Planning System*. Published for the Office of the Deputy Prime Minster by The Stationery Office.

Planning Policy Wales (2009) *TAN 5: Nature Conservation and Planning*. Welsh Assembly Government.

Scottish Executive (2004) *Scotland's Biodiversity: It's in Your Hands – A strategy for the conservation and enhancement of biodiversity in Scotland*. The Scottish Government. http://www.scotland.gov.uk/ Resource/Doc/25954/0014583.pdf

Scottish Planning Policy (2010) *A statement of the Scottish Government's policy on nationally important land use planning matters*. The Scottish Government. http://www.scotland.gov.uk/ Resource/Doc/300760/0093908.pdf

Treweek, J. (1999) *Ecological Impact Assessment*. Blackwell Science.

Treweek, J., Trewhella, W. & Barker, J. (2007) *Principles of ecoapractice and future developments*. In: *Advances in Ecological Impact Assessment for Mammals*. The Mammal Society's Autumn Symposium 23rd – 25th November 2007, London Zoo.

# Red Squirrel

*Figure 2.1.* Red squirrel in summer without ear tufts and showing its bright, orange-red coat.
[Peter Lurz].

## 2.  Red Squirrel
*By John Gurnell and Peter W. W. Lurz*

### 2.1.  Background Biology

The red squirrel *Sciurus vulgaris* (**Fig. 2.1**) belongs to the Order Rodentia, Family Sciuridae, Subfamily Sciurinae. The information below is taken mainly from Gurnell *et al*. (2008) and Lurz *et al*. (2008).

Sexes are similar and red squirrels in the UK are 180–240 mm in length (head and body) with a tail of 140–195 mm. Observed body mass for adults ranges from 260 to 360 g. Upper fur colour is variable from deep brown or even black to reddish-brown or chestnut to grey brown. The underside is pale, white or cream. Blond or bleached tails or tail tips are observed in some individuals in northern England, especially the western populations, and in Scotland. Dark coloured individuals occur in some parts of Scotland. Characteristic ear tufts grow in late summer and are large during the winter but gradually thin to being small during the summer.

Red squirrels are adapted to climbing and leaping with long hind limbs, long toes with long curved claws, and distinctive and well-developed bushy tails that are used for balance, as well as for signalling and thermoregulation. Their primary foods are the seeds and fruits of trees, but they are opportunists and take a wide variety of other food types when available or when tree seeds are scarce. Items include fungi, berries, buds, shoots and flowers. Tree bark may be stripped to gain access to the sap below. Squirrels are also known to occasionally take invertebrates (e.g. caterpillars), lichen and bird eggs or nestlings. Seeds are scatterhoarded in the autumn and the fruiting bodies of fungi are cached on branches in trees.

Red squirrels are solitary, do not form pair-bonds, and males do not contribute to the parental care of the young. Communal nesting may occur in the winter and spring between familial animals (e.g. siblings). The mating system of red squirrels is polygynous-promiscuous. Females are polyoestrous and are in heat for only one day during each oestrous cycle. They are capable of producing two litters of one to six young each (occasionally more). There are two breeding peaks within a year, with mating in winter and spring leading to spring-born (February–April) and summer-born (May–August) litters, respectively. Precise timing may vary depending on food availability and weather (e.g. abundant autumn seed crops combined with mild winters may lead to early breeding). There is little courtship prior to mating apart from a 'mating chase' in which males are attracted to a female in heat by her scent and follow her for up to several hours. The leading male in the following group tends to be heaviest and dominant and reportedly accounts for most matings.

Red squirrels are active all year and do not hibernate. Activity is reduced in winter to one main active phase and rises to two phases during the summer. Poor weather conditions may reduce activity especially in winter. Red squirrels are not generally territorial although breeding females with litters may space themselves out. Otherwise home range overlap among individuals can be extensive. Home range size and spacing behaviour varies with sexual activity, habitat quality, and seasonal changes in tree seed availability.

### 2.2.  Habitat Requirements

Red squirrels are found in most woodland habitats, ranging from conifer forests and plantations to

*Figure 2.2.* **Red squirrel habitat.**
Left: good red squirrel habitat, namely Scots pine forest in northern Scotland. Right: Sitka spruce plantation, Glentress Forest, Borders, Scotland; although not particularly good habitat, red squirrels can survive in these extensive plantations found, for example, in the north of England and Scotland.
[Peter Lurz; Crown Copyright 2012].

broadleaf woodlands and copses, suburban parks and gardens (*Fig. 2.2*). Squirrel presence and habitat use is influenced by the age of the trees (they have to be old enough to produce seeds) and the species of trees and shrubs present. They survive well in both broadleaf woods, especially those with plentiful hazelnuts, and conifer forests. Average densities are around one squirrel per hectare for Scots pine *Pinus sylvestris* or mixed woodlands and can reach similar levels in broadleaf woodland. However, densities tend to be lower for spruce dominated plantation forests (*Table 2.1*). For comparison, grey squirrels *Sciurus carolinensis* have similar densities to red squirrels in conifer forests but much higher densities in deciduous forests.

*Table 2.1.* Typical red squirrel densities in different types of woodland (modified from Gurnell *et al.* 2009).

| No. ha -1 | Forest type/Region | Dominant tree species |
|---|---|---|
| 0.00 – 0.11 | Conifer/northern England | Sitka spruce |
| 0.33 | Conifer/Scotland | Scots pine |
| 0.31 – 0.43 | Conifer/northern England | Lodgepole pine |
| 0.21 – 0.41 | Conifer/northern England | Norway spruce |
| 0.68 – 1.21 | Suburban/Jersey | Oak, sweet chestnut, Scots pine |
| 0.90 | Deciduous/southern England | Oak – hazel |
| 0.50 – 0.81 | Deciduous/northern England | Oak – hazel |

Squirrels live in nests called dreys (*Fig. 2.3*). These are spherical, c.30 cm in diameter but sometimes larger, and situated close to the trunk of a tree or in a fork in the branches, usually, but not always, above 6 m in height. Climbing plants such as ivy often obscure dreys. Outer layers consist of twigs, sometimes with needles or leaves attached; the inner cavity (12–16 cm diameter) is lined with soft material such as moss, leaves, needles, clipped dry grass, and bark. The inner lining consists mainly of grass and moss. Holes in trees may be used as dens, especially in broadleaf woods, and owl nest boxes may sometimes be occupied by squirrels.

## 2.3. Status and Distribution

Populations of red squirrel in the UK have declined dramatically over the last 50–75 years, being replaced by the larger (adult body weight 500–600 g) grey squirrel, first introduced from North America in the late 1800s. Red squirrels are now only found in parts of the north of England, Scotland, Wales and Northern Ireland, although island populations persist in Poole Harbour in Dorset, and on the Isle of Wight (*Fig. 2.4*). In Ireland red squirrels are extinct in Meath and Westmeath but still considered

common in many areas, especially west of the river Shannon. Grey squirrels have significantly increased their range in the past decade and are present in 26 counties with the most notable spread over the last years in the eastern counties of Antrim, Wicklow and Wexford. They have also breached the river Shannon in a few locations and may begin to extend their range west (Carey *et al.* 2007). Red squirrels are usually displaced within 2–15 years of the arrival of greys (e.g. Gurnell *et al.* 2004; Wauters *et al.* 2005).

## 2.4. Legislative Protection

In England, Wales and Scotland, red squirrels are protected by their inclusion on Schedules 5 and 6 of the Wildlife and Countryside Act 1981 (as amended). The Act makes it an offence to intentionally (or, in Scotland, recklessly) kill, injure or take any red squirrel, or to intentionally or recklessly damage, destroy, or obstruct access to any structure or place used by a red squirrel for shelter or protection, or to disturb a red squirrel while it is occupying a structure or place used for shelter or protection. It is also illegal to keep, transport, sell, exchange or offer for sale or exchange any animal or any part or derivative of one, if obtained after 10th June 1994. The Act also prohibits certain methods of killing, injuring or taking wild animals.

Red squirrels are similarly protected in Northern Ireland by their inclusion on Schedules 5 and 6 of the Wildlife Order (NI) 1985 (as amended). In England, Wales and Scotland, red squirrels are also protected under the Wild Mammals (Protection) Act 1996 which makes it illegal to subject them to any willful act of cruelty or abuse and, additionally in Scotland, by the Nature Conservation (Scotland) Act 2004 whereby anyone perceived to have committed any offences must be able to demonstrate that they have taken 'reasonable precautions' to avoid or minimise the damage to red squirrels. Similarly, in Northern Ireland the Welfare of Animals Act (NI) 2011 could be applied in cases where any willful act causes suffering.

It is possible to get licences from the country agencies for some activities that may affect red squirrels such as scientific research or education, conservation and photography. Licences may also be issued to preserve public health or safety, prevent the spread of disease or prevent serious damage to crops, growing timber or any other form of property. However, there is no provision for licensing development activities under the Wildlife and Countryside Act in England and Wales, although a developer could seek to rely on a defence of 'an incidental result of an otherwise lawful activity that could not reasonably have been avoided' if the developer was found to be in breach of the Act. In Scotland, the Wildlife and

*Figure 2.3.* **A squirrel drey in an oak tree.**
[Crown Copyright 2012].

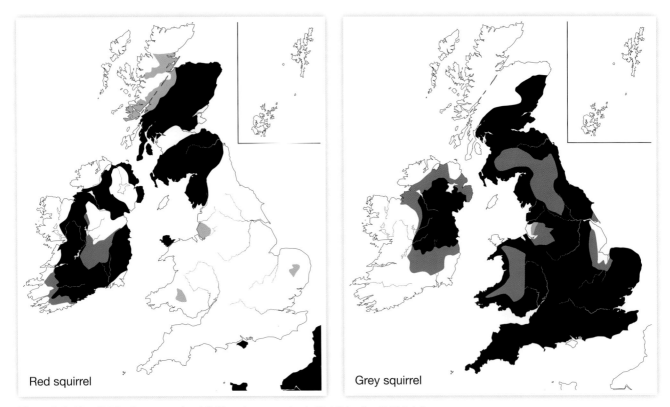

*Figure 2.4.* **The distribution map of red (left) and grey squirrels (right) for the British Isles.**
Black indicates regular or usual range; dark grey, scattered but regular occurrence; light grey, rare occurrences, vagrants, or scarce and beyond the regular range. Note that the grey squirrel has not yet been completely eradicated from Anglesey. There is also a population of red squirrel in north-east Wales in the Clocaenog Forest (on the Conwy/Denbighshire border, in Clwyd). The mid-Wales forest population is slightly to the north of the position shown on the map (on the Powys/Ceredigion/Carmathenshire border). There are no red squirrels near the north-east border of Wales. There are no red squirrels in East Anglia.
[from: Harris & Yalden (2008) *Mammals of the British Isles: Handbook,* 4th edition. Mammal Society; with minor amendments].

Natural Environment (Scotland) Act 2011 inserts a new clause 'for any other social, economic or environmental purpose' into section 16 of the Wildlife and Countryside Act 1981. The effect is that Scottish Ministers can license the disturbance of squirrels provided that the activity licensed will make a significant contribution to the achievement of a significant social, economic or environmental benefit, and there is no other satisfactory solution. The power to grant licences has been delegated to SNH and guidance on protected species licensing can be found on the SNH website: http://www.snh.org.uk. The Wildlife and Natural Environment Act (Northern Ireland) 2011 changes, wording of offences under Article 10(1) and (4) (protection of certain wild animals including the red squirrel) of the Wildlife Order (NI) 1985 from an 'intentional act' to an 'intentional or reckless act'.

In Ireland, red squirrels are protected under the Irish Wildlife Act (1976) and the Irish Wildlife Amendment Act (2000); they are listed as 'Near threatened' in the *Ireland Red List No. 3: Terrestrial Mammals* (Marnell *et al.* 2009, further details can be found on the National Parks and Wildlife Service website: http://www.npws.ie).

Red squirrels are not protected under the Conservation of Habitats and Species Regulations 2010, as they are still widespread and abundant in Europe, although grey squirrels are present in Italy and currently expanding their range at the expense of red squirrels (Bertolino *et al.* 2009; Martinoli *et al.* 2010).

## 2.5. Summary of UK BAP Status and Recommended Actions

The red squirrel was listed as a UK BAP species in 1995, and is on the Biodiversity Lists for England and Wales (listed as a Species of Principal Importance under the NERC Act, 2006), Scotland (under the Nature Conservation (Scotland) Act 2004), and Northern Ireland (listed as a Priority Species in the Northern Ireland Priority Species List, March 2010).

The main objectives of the original UK Red Squirrel Action Plan were to: where appropriate, maintain and enhance current red squirrel populations and re-establish red squirrel populations, with contributory actions; to ensure effective implementation of relevant legislation, improve knowledge through conservation research and advice, promote education, and awareness of red squirrel conservation; and to survey and monitor red squirrel populations (see Pepper & Patterson 1998). BAP targets for each country were established in 2006 (links to country groups and individual country action plans can be found on the UK Red Squirrel Group website,

http://www.ukredsquirrels.org): Northern Ireland and the Republic of Ireland also have a joint red squirrel action plan (Anon 2008).

The current BAP recommended actions for the red squirrel are (http://www.jncc.gov.uk/_speciespages/565.pdf):

- prepare and implement site management plans for key sites (squirrel reserves, priority sites and strongholds), covering the whole range of site-based measures, to safeguard long-term viability of the species;

- improve understanding of the transmission and mode of action of squirrel pox virus (SQPV) and develop ways of reducing its impact on red squirrel populations;

- develop a suite of best practice survey and monitoring methods and use these to determine the status and trends in red (and grey) squirrel populations throughout the UK.

## 2.6. Survey Methodology

*Distinguishing red and grey squirrels in the field*

The red squirrel and the introduced grey squirrel can sometimes be confused in the field (*Fig. 2.5*), especially since grey squirrels may exhibit some reddish-brown colouration on their normally grey backs and sides, and some red squirrels may have a lot of grey colour in their coat. The dorsal fur of the grey squirrel is mainly grey but may exhibit some reddish-brown colouration over the back and down the limbs. The underside is greyish-white. The tail of the grey squirrel is of a grizzled grey colour and this species has only small, inconspicuous ear tufts in winter. Melanic (dark) grey squirrels can be found in Hertfordshire, Cambridgeshire and Bedfordshire and melanic red squirrels are reported from Argyll, Scotland. Dark-tailed red squirrels have been observed in Cumbria in winter.

Dreys, tracks and feeding signs (*Fig. 2.6*) of red and grey squirrels are similar and practically impossible to tell apart. The forefeet of squirrels have four toes which point forwards, and four closely aligned pads on their palms, about 25 mm wide. The hind feet have five toes, with four oval plantar pads and one hind plantar pad, about 40 mm long, 35 mm wide. Tracks are characteristic with forefeet behind and inside the line of the larger hind feet, a stride of about 35 cm, hops of less than 1 m, and tail held high so that tail marks are seldom visible. Tree bark is sometimes scratched in particular places, especially on frequently used pathways, up tree trunks or underneath large branches. Hazelnuts are split open leaving two pieces of shell with clean edges (cf. mice and voles), and characteristic 'cores' of conifer cones can frequently be found, together with piles of stripped scales distinct from split edges made by birds. Feeding remains can be

*Figure 2.5.* **Red and grey squirrel forms.**
Top left: red squirrel on tree with ear tufts, Northumberland, with grey-red coat. Top right: very dark red squirrel, Cumbria. Bottom left: grey squirrel. Bottom right: melanic grey squirrel.
[James Leonard; Alastair Craig Baxter; Christoph Cramer; Reid Cooper].

*Figure 2.6.* Squirrelled Sitka spruce cone (left) contrasted with a cone processed by a wood mouse.
[Peter Lurz].

scattered or grouped on, for example, tree stumps. Locations near the base of other trees are favoured to allow a rapid escape into the canopy.

Bark may be stripped from the base, stem or crown of trees, particularly pole-stage trees 10–40 years old. Incisor tooth marks may be found on fungi (larger than those of mice and voles and not ragged like bird pecks or irregular and slimy like slug feeding). Red squirrels are considered to be more arboreal than grey squirrels and may spend 70 % or more of their active period in the canopy of trees, although foraging on the ground for seeds such as fallen beech *Fagus* sp. mast or fallen Norway spruce *Picea abies* cones in spring following an autumn mast crop may be extensive.

### Survey methods

Red squirrels predominately live in woods and forests and are seldom found in cities and towns in Britain. However, they frequently travel along hedgerows between woods and use shelter belts and small groups of trees in more open landscapes. They also frequent people's gardens in rural areas, often using feeders put out especially for them or for birds. Therefore no habitats that contain trees or hedgerows can be ignored when surveying for red squirrels.

To inform any project proposal and before carrying out a survey, the following are all good sources of information: survey maps, Google and other online maps, aerial photographs, or digital land cover maps if available. Area, type of tree cover (e.g. broadleaf, coniferous), approximate forest age (e.g. clearfell, young plantation, mature), and the position of roads, rides, bridleways and paths can be determined from maps and will help plan where survey activities might take place. Where relevant, forest management plans (e.g. felling, thinning, replanting) should also be consulted. Armed with this information, a visit to the site and an initial, broad scale survey should be carried out. Carrying out an initial survey is straightforward and involves walking through the different blocks of woodland stopping every 50 m or so and recording information about tree species, age, density and potential seed crops, and squirrel signs such as dreys and feeding remains. This gives a rough idea about the potential squirrel carrying capacity (denoted K) of the forest blocks (low, moderate or high), and about current squirrel occupation of the forest (few signs, some signs, many signs) (*Fig. 2.7*). The main survey or surveys can then be planned and carried out according to the reasons why they are being done, and taking into account, where appropriate, the sample size and power of the surveying and monitoring methods to detect a real change in population numbers (see Gurnell *et al*. 2009).

Non-invasive survey methods, that is those that do not require trapping or handling animals, cannot confirm the absence of red squirrels, which can occur at low densities (e.g. one squirrel per 10 ha of forest), and some methods are not able to distinguish between red and grey squirrels (*Table 2.2*). Visual surveys and hair tube/feeder box/feeder station surveys are the best ones to use to assess whether red squirrels are present and it is important to plan surveys with sufficient effort and replication in order to successfully detect them; full details of all methods are provided by Gurnell *et al*. (2009). Studies are currently taking place on the

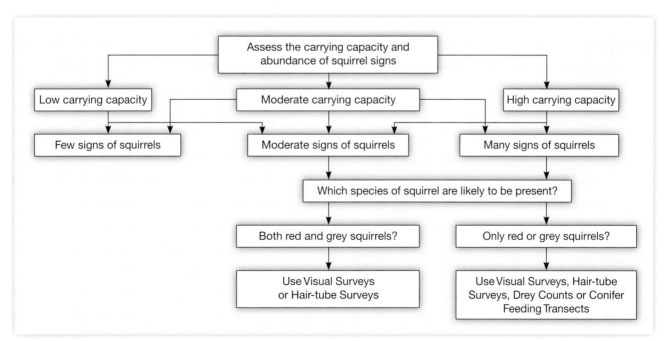

*Figure 2.7.* Decision tree for use when considering techniques to survey or monitor squirrels, based on information gathered in the initial survey.
[modified from Gurnell *et al*. 2009].

*Table 2.2.* Squirrel survey methods (modified from Gurnell *et al.* 2009).

| | Method | Can it detect squirrel presence? | Can it distinguish red from grey? | How good is it for estimating densities? | What type of woodland? |
|---|---|---|---|---|---|
| 1 | Visual surveys | Yes | Yes | Moderate | All* |
| 2 | Hair tube and feeder box/feeder station surveys | Yes | Yes | Poor – Moderate | All |
| 3 | Drey counts | Not always** | No | Poor – Moderate | All* |
| 4 | Feeding transects | Yes | No | Moderate | Conifer |
| 5 | Whole maize bait | Yes | No | Not appropriate | All |
| 6 | Nest boxes | Yes | Yes | Poor | All |

*Poor results in dense conifer plantations. **Dreys may be abandoned but may take some time to fall into disrepair.

Visual surveys involve direct sightings of squirrels made during a standard time period and over a standard area (i.e. standardised time–area counts). In the longer term, repeating the survey once or twice a year, e.g. in spring and autumn, for a number of years enables changes in numbers over time to be monitored, but counts can be carried out at any time, with late winter/spring being the best because there are no leaves on deciduous trees to obscure canopy visibility. If the weather is unsuitable then the survey should be postponed. Squirrels are unlikely to be very active in heavy rain, strong winds or when it is very cold. The surveys can be repeated two to four times within a two-week period to take into account variations in weather and squirrel activity. Surveys lines can be baited to improve detection rates (see Gurnell *et al.* 2011).

Cone feeding transect surveys involve walking a transect 1 m wide and 25 m long, and removing cone remains every few weeks to assess how much squirrel feeding has taken place (*Fig. 2.8*).

Hair surveys make use of specially adapted lengths of plastic drainpipe, which are baited to attract squirrels (Gurnell & Pepper 1994), or feeding boxes (*Fig. 2.9*). Hairs are collected on sticky tapes inside the tubes or the box entrance as the animals enter to get food. Collected hair is removed from the tubes periodically for examination. Hair surveys can be labour and equipment expensive and training is required to identify the hairs from the two squirrel species. However, they are good for detecting the presence of squirrels and if calibrated by carrying

effectiveness of using camera traps in systematic surveys for squirrels (Gurnell *unpubl.*).

out comparative trials with other methods can provide an index of population trends (see Bertolino *et al.* 2009). In general, however, unless calibrated with live trapping methods in specific types of habitat, non-invasive survey methods are not useful for obtaining absolute estimates of population size.

## 2.7. Impact Assessment, Mitigation, Compensation and Enhancement

Red squirrel habitats can be altered by a variety of activities, including road building, recreational and housing developments, agriculture and forestry operations (*Fig. 2.10*). Habitat fragmentation can be equally as important as habitat loss. Building roads or tracks through established woodland is a good example of a project that can result in habitat loss and fragmentation, and the process of road building can be a major disturbance to red squirrels. Such impacts can lead to the outright loss of feeding and nesting habitat and thus lower the number of squirrels that can be supported by the remaining woodland area (carrying capacity) or affect the age structure of the woodland and the amount of mature forest available that can produce seed. They can also lead to fragmentation and isolation leading to localised, small populations and increase both mortality rates (e.g. increased risk during dispersal of road mortalities) and risk of local population extinction. Direct mortality can also occur when trees containing dreys are felled during the breeding period.

Significant effects on red squirrels could arise from loss or fragmentation of habitat or a change that might facilitate incursion by grey squirrels. Whether a project would give rise to a significant effect on the red squirrel population can be determined by asking the following questions:

- will the project impact mortality or breeding at a scale which would affect the viability of the population?

- will the project fragment the population and lead to an increased risk of local extinction or increased mortality as a result of forced dispersal over unsuitable habitat or areas with no or limited cover?

- does the age structure of the affected forest habitat provide sufficient mature habitat able to produce seed to ensure a dependable long-term food supply?

- will the project increase the likelihood of grey squirrel immigration or affect the 'defendability' of the area in terms of grey squirrel encroachment.

If the answer to any of the above questions is yes, then the proposals could have a significant negative effect on the conservation status of the red squirrel populations. This would be a key impact to

*Figure 2.8.* **Cone feeding transect surveys.**
A transect is walked and cone remains removed at regular intervals to assess how much squirrel feeding has been taking place.
[Peter Lurz].

*Figure 2.9.* **Hair survey tubes.**
Close up showing tube and sticky pad with hair attached (left). Hair survey tube in position (right).
[Crown Copyright 2012].

*Figure 2.10.* A harvester felling Sitka spruce plantation in Kielder Forest, Northumberland, England.
[Crown Copyright 2012].

*Figure 2.11.* Red squirrel rope bridges.
A rope bridge across a road on Jersey, Channel Islands (left). Red squirrel on a rope bridge (right).
[John Gurnell; Crown Copyright 2012].

address in EcIA. Even if the effects of a project are not likely to be significant, but would be demonstrably negative (for example a reduction in available habitat which did not threaten population viability) then mitigation measures should be applied.

Well before the planned start of site clearance, the area should be surveyed for the presence of squirrels (e.g. using visual counts or feeding transects and drey counts and, where possible, drey trees should be marked). If squirrels are present, the following guidelines should be followed (also see Gurnell & Pepper 1991; 1993; 1994 and Pepper & Patterson 1998 with respect to forestry operations):

- during the breeding season (generally February to September) avoid felling trees containing dreys. Advice should be obtained from the appropriate forestry authority such as the Forestry Commission before any tree felling is started;

- outside the breeding season, avoid isolating stands of trees during tree removal so that squirrels can relocate;

- for felling operations, consider approaches that reduce the impact of harvesting such as small coupe sizes, or continuous cover silvicultural options (Mason *et al.* 1999) in areas where windthrow risks are low;

- in order to increase red squirrel carrying capacity in remnant habitat following loss due to development, consider new plantings to compensate for tree removal;

- consider reconnecting forests after land-use change by planting corridors of trees, hedgerows and rope bridges or green bridges across roads.

Red squirrels are often killed on roads, especially during the autumn when squirrels disperse. Road mortalities may increase where new roads are built through woodland.

Rope bridges of up to 20 m or more have been erected across roads to both reduce the effects of habitat fragmentation and reduce road deaths (*Fig 2.11*). Rope bridges should typically be placed at least 7 m above the road (to allow normal traffic to pass underneath) and should be covered by public liability insurance.

Green bridges (more substantial structures with growing vegetation) have also been proposed to mitigate against the negative effects of building new roads through woodland and could be used to reduce fragmentation for a suite of different species, not just red squirrels.

Squirrel warning signs can also be placed on roads, but unless erected on private land, need permission from the relevant highways authority.

### Managing disease threat

SQPV is a good example of a pathogen-mediated competitive agent involving an invasive species (the grey squirrel) and a native species (the red squirrel) (Tompkins *et al.* 2002; Gurnell *et al.* 2006; Sainsbury *et al.* 2008; Carroll *et al.* 2009; Bruemmer *et al.* 2010). SQPV causes disease with high mortality in red squirrels but appears non-pathogenic in grey squirrels, which act as reservoir hosts. It has been demonstrated that the replacement of red squirrels by grey squirrels is some 20 times faster in those areas where grey squirrels carry the virus (Rushton *et al.* 2006). Therefore, it is important to minimise contact and the probability of transmission of the SQPV and other pathogens from grey to red squirrels. Projects and their resulting mitigation should therefore avoid creating grey squirrel invasion routes within the landscape surrounding the area (Gurnell *et al.* 2006).

Red squirrels take food put out for birds in gardens, and sometimes squirrel feeders are specifically deployed to attract red squirrels or as a mitigation measure to assist populations after disturbance. In the absence of grey squirrels, supplementary feeding may benefit red squirrels, such as on the island of Jersey in the Channel Islands (Magris & Gurnell 2002). However, focal feed stations may increase the spread of viruses such as SQPV to red squirrels as feed stations will be used by both red and grey squirrels (Bruemmer *et al.* 2010). Advice on supplementary feeding can be found at the UK Red Squirrel Group website; importantly, supplementary feeding in areas where both squirrel species co-occur should not form part of any mitigation efforts, and this information should be made known to local people.

### Red squirrel reintroduction

If a project is likely to lead to remnant populations that are very small (e.g. < 20 individuals) and potentially unviable, then translocating the animals to new areas or even removal of animals into captivity, may be a last resort. However, any action needs to consider a number of key points. The capture and translocation of wild red squirrels requires a licence from the respective licensing authority. Furthermore, release sites that have landowner support will need to be selected carefully, examining forest composition and age structure to ensure that they can support a viable population. Areas that contain grey squirrels, or sites that already support an existing, viable red squirrel population, need to be avoided. Red squirrel translocations and reintroductions as a conservation tactic have been considered by Venning *et al.* (1997) and the health and welfare issues of squirrels involved in reintroductions, including transmitting disease to a new location, by

Sainsbury & Gurnell (1995;1997). Reintroductions of red squirrels on the Island of Anglesey off the north-west coast of Wales demonstrate that these methods can be successful if the grey squirrels, the reason for their loss, have first been removed (Shuttleworth 2004).

## 2.8. Research Requirements

Red squirrel conservation research requirements include SQPV and vaccine development, identifying, managing and monitoring priority red squirrel conservation sites, methods of controlling grey squirrels, effectiveness of red squirrel translocations and effects of climate change (see UK Red Squirrel Group website). Key research requirements with respect to survey before, and mitigation following, projects include:

- to look at ways to refine non-invasive survey techniques that can distinguish red and grey squirrels, particularly with respect to:
  - improving detection rates;
  - different types of habitat (e.g. habitat corridors, small woodlands, different types of woodland, e.g. coniferous, deciduous, mixed);
  - sampling effort and the power to detect changes in population size within an area;
- to consider habitat manipulations, e.g. tree plantings, the provision of extra food, and the use of nest boxes, that will benefit red squirrels in the short (1 – 5 years) and longer term (> 5 years) after projects and that will also be less favourable to grey squirrels;
- to study the effectiveness of rope bridges and green bridges in reconnecting habitat and reducing red squirrel road mortalities.

## 2.9. References and Bibliography

Anon (2008) *All-Ireland Species Action Plan, Red Squirrel* Sciurus vulgaris. 19. National Parks & Wildlife Service, Dublin/Environment & Heritage Service, Belfast.

Bertolino, S., Lurz, P. W. W., Sanderson, R. & Rushton, S. P. (2008) Predicting the spread of the American grey squirrel (*Sciurus carolinensis*) in Europe: A call for a co-ordinated European approach. *Biological Conservation* **141**: 2564–2575.

Bertolino, S., Wauters, L., Pizzul, A., Molinari, A., Lurz, P. & Tosi, G. (2009) A general approach of using hair-tubes to monitor the European red squirrel: a method applicable at regional and national scales. *Mammalian Biology* **74**: 210–219.

Bosch, S, & Lurz, P.W.W. (2012) *The Eurasian Red Squirrel* Sciurus vulgaris. NBB English.

Bruemmer, C. M., Rushton, S. P., Gurnell, J., Lurz, P. W., Nettleton, P., Sainsbury, A. W., Duff, J. P., Gilray, J. & McInnes, C. J. (2010) Epidemiology of squirrelpox virus in grey squirrels in the UK. *Epidemiology and Infection* **138**: 941–950.

Carey, M., Hamilton, G., Poole, A. & Lawton, C. (2007) *The Irish Squirrel Survey 2007*. National Council for Forest Research and Development, Dublin, Ireland.

Carroll, B., Russell, P., Gurnell, J., Nettleton, P. & Sainsbury, A. W. (2009) Epidemics of squirrelpox virus disease in red squirrels (*Sciurus vulgaris*): temporal and serological findings. *Epidemiology and Infection* **137**: 257–265.

Countryside Council for Wales (2009) *Conservation plan for red squirrels in Wales prepared by the Welsh Squirrel Forum*. 12 pp. Countryside Council for Wales, Bangor, Gwynedd.

Everest, D. J., Grierson, S. S., Meredith, A. L. & Milne, E. M. (2010) Adenovirus in a red squirrel (*Sciurus vulgaris*) from Scotland. *The Veterinary Record* **167**: 184.

Forestry Commission (2007) *Tree felling: getting permission*. FCSS100. 7 pp. Forestry Commission, Edinburgh.

Gurnell, J. (1999) Grey squirrels in woodlands: managing grey squirrels to prevent woodland damage. *Enact* **7**: 10–14.

Gurnell, J. & Mayle, B. (2004) Increasing efficiency of controlling grey squirrels in conifer habitats. *Forestry & British Timber* 16–19.

Gurnell, J. & Pepper, H. (1991) Conserving the red squirrel. *Research Information Note 205.* pp 4. Forestry Commission, Edinburgh.

Gurnell, J. & Pepper, H. (1993) A critical look at conserving the British red squirrel *Sciurus vulgaris*. *Mammal Review* **23**: 125–136.

Gurnell, J. & Pepper, H. (1994) Red squirrel conservation field study methods. *Research Information Note 255*, p. 10. Forestry Commission, Edinburgh.

Gurnell, J., Lurz, P. W. W., McDonald, R. & Pepper, H. (2009) Practical techniques for surveying and monitoring squirrels. *Forestry Commission Practice Note 11*, pp. 1–12, FC Alice Holt Lodge, Farnham, Surrey, UK.

Gurnell, J., Lurz, P. W. W. & Halliwell, E. (2008) Red squirrel *Sciurus vulgaris*. In: *Mammals of the British Isles: Handbook,* 4th edition (eds) S. Harris & D. W. Yalden). The Mammal Society.

Gurnell, J., McDonald, R. & Lurz, P. W. W. (2011) Making red squirrels more visible: the use of baited visual counts to monitor populations. *Mammal Review* **41**: 244–250.

Gurnell, J., Rushton, S. P., Lurz, P. W. W., Sainsbury, A. W., Nettleton, P., Shirley, M. D. F., Bruemmer, C. & Geddes, N. (2006) Squirrel poxvirus: Landscape scale strategies for managing disease threat. *Biological Conservation* **131**: 287–295.

Gurnell, J., Wauters, L. A., Lurz, P. W. W. & Tosi, G. (2004) Alien species and interspecific competition: effects of introduced eastern grey squirrels on red squirrel population dynamics. *Journal of Animal Ecology* **73**: 26–35.

Lurz, P. W. W., Gurnell, J. & Magris, L. (2005) *Sciurus vulgaris*. *Mammalian Species* **769**: 1–10.

Lurz, P., Shirley, M. & Geddes, N. (2008) Monitoring low density populations: a perspective on what level of population decline we can truly detect. *Animal Biodiversity and Conservation* **31**: 29–39.

Magris, L. & Gurnell, J. (2002) Population ecology of the red squirrel (*Sciurus vulgaris*) in a fragmented woodland ecosystem on the island of Jersey, Channel Islands. *Journal of Zoology, London* **256**: 99–112.

Marnell, F., Kingston, N. & Looney, D. (2009) *Irish Red List No. 3 – Terrestrial Mammals*. National Parks and Wildlife Service, Department of the Environment, Heritage and Local Government, Dublin, Ireland.

Martinoli, A., Bertolino, S., Preatoni, D. G., Balduzzi, A., Marsan, A., Genovesi, P., Tosi, G., & Wauters, L. A. (2010) Headcount 2010: the multiplication of the grey squirrel introduced to Italy. *Hystrix* **21**: 127–136.

Mason, W., Kerr, G. & Simpson, J. (1999) What is continuous cover forestry? *FC Information Note No. 29*. 8 pp. Forestry Commission, Edinburgh.

Mayle, B., Ferryman, M. & Pepper, H. (2007) Controlling grey squirrel damage to woodlands. *Practice Note 4*. p. 16: Forestry Commission.

Pepper, H. & Patterson, G. (1998) Red squirrel conservation. *Practice Note 5*. p. 8. Forestry Commission (Revised 2001).

Parrot, D., Quy, R., Van Driel, K., Lurz, P., Rushton, S., Gurnell, J., Aebischer, N. & Reynolds, J. (2009) *Review of red squirrel conservation activity in Northern England*. Natural England Commissioned Report NECR019. pp 109. Natural England. http://naturalengland.etraderstores.com/NaturalEngland

Parrot, D., Quy, R., Somerwill, K., Lurz, P. W., Rushton, S. & Gurnell, J. (2010) *Mapping red squirrel conservation effort In the North of England*. pp 53. Natural England, Sheffield.

Rushton, S. P., Lurz, P. W. W., Gurnell, J. & Fuller, R. (2000) Modelling the spatial dynamics of parapoxvirus disease in red and grey squirrels: a possible cause of the decline in the red squirrel in the UK? *Journal of Applied Ecology* **37**: 997–1012.

Rushton, S. P., Lurz, P. W. W., Gurnell, J., Nettleton, P., Bruemmer, C., Shirley, M. D. F. & Sainsbury, A. W. (2006) Disease threats posed by alien species: the role of a poxvirus in the decline of the native red squirrel in Britain. *Epidemiology and Infection* **134**: 521–533.

Sainsbury, A. & Gurnell, J. (1995) An investigation into the health and welfare of red squirrels, *Sciurus vulgaris*, involved in reintroductions studies. *The Veterinary Record* **137**: 367–370.

Sainsbury, A. & Gurnell, J. (1997) Disease risks associated with the translocation of squirrels, Sciuridae, in Europe. *The Journal of the British Veterinary Zoological Society* **2**: 5–8.

Sainsbury, A. W., Deaville, R., Lawson, B., Cooley, W. A., Farelly, S. S., Stack, M. J., Duff, P., McInnes, C. J., Gurnell, J., Russell, P. H., Rushton, S. P., Pfeiffer, D. U., Nettleton, P. & Lurz, P. W. (2008) Poxviral disease in red squirrels *Sciurus vulgaris* in the UK: spatial and temporal trends of an emerging threat. *Ecohealth* **5**: 305–316.

Shuttleworth, C. (1999) The use of nest boxes by the red squirrel *Sciurus vulgaris* in a coniferous habitat. *Mammal Review* **29**: 61–66.

Shuttleworth, C. (2004) Grey Squirrel Control on the Island of Anglesey, a report to the Countryside Council for Wales. Menter Môn, unpublished report.

Shuttleworth, C., Jackson, N. & Kenward, R. (2009) *The reintroduction of the red squirrel* Sciurus vulgaris *to Newborough forest, North Wales: A five year project review*. Menter Môn, unpublished report. pp 61.

Tompkins, D. M., Sainsbury, A. W., Nettleton, P., Buxton, D. & Gurnell, J. (2002) Parapoxvirus causes a deleterious disease in red squirrels associated with UK population declines. *Proceedings of the Royal Society – Biological Sciences* **269**: 529–533.

Venning, T., Sainsbury, A. & Gurnell, J. (1997) An experimental study on translocating red squirrels to Thetford Forest. In: *The Conservation of Red Squirrels,* Sciurus vulgaris L (eds) Gurnell, J. & Lurz, P.), pp 133–143. People's Trust for Endangered Species, London.

Wauters, L., Tosi, G. & Gurnell, J. (2005) A review of the competitive effects of alien grey squirrels on behaviour, activity and habitat use of red squirrels in mixed, deciduous woodland in Italy. *Hystrix – Italian Journal of Mammalogy* **16**: 27.

## Acknowledgements

*The authors would like to thank Brenda Mayle of the Forestry Commission for her help with this chapter.*

# Harvest Mouse

*Figure 3.1.* Harvest mouse.
[Mike Taylor/Seeing].

## 3.    Harvest Mouse
*By Simone Bullion*

### 3.1.  Background Biology

Harvest mice are the smallest British rodent, weighing little more than 6 g when adult. These tiny mice have golden fur, with a pale belly and a semi-prehensile tail (*Figs. 3.1* and *3.2*). Their small size and excellent climbing ability enables them to occupy the stalk zone of grasses during the summer and autumn months, constructing woven nests which are an excellent indicator of their presence. In late autumn and winter, as the vegetation dies back, they switch to a much more terrestrial lifestyle. Their diet is varied, including flowers, insects, seeds and berries.

Breeding starts in May and can last until December, although this is dependent upon weather. Several litters are born each season, averaging 4 – 5 young in each. Populations fluctuate annually with a peak in numbers during late autumn, falling steeply by February and March. Cold, wet weather in autumn and sudden frosts can cause significant mortality in late-born litters. They are active through a 24 hour period, so are taken by a wide range of mammalian and avian predators, including mustelids, foxes, owls, hawks and corvids. They account for around 2 % of mammal prey taken by domestic cats (Woods *et al*. 2003) and an even smaller percentage for barn owls (Love *et al*. 2000).

The debate as to whether harvest mice are native or a post-glacial introduction is now resolved in favour of them being indigenous to Great Britain, following the finding of early post-glacial fossil evidence (Price 2003).

### 3.2.  Habitat Requirements

Harvest mice occupy a wide range of habitats and are sometimes regarded as a wetland species (Perrow & Jowitt 1995). They can be found in rough and tussocky grassland, ungrazed and uncut meadows, reedbeds and riparian margins, as well as roadside verges and arable field margins (*Fig. 3.3*), but rarely occur in cereal crops. They are often recorded in young plantations within the associated rank grassland, but are rarely found in mature woodland. In the arable landscape, field margins are of particular importance and they will also readily colonise rough grassland left as 'beetle banks'. Harvest mice also build nests and forage within millet when planted as wild bird cover.

Summer nests (*Fig. 3.4*) are built within a diverse range of grass species such as cock's-foot *Dactylis glomerata*, common reed *Phragmites australis*, reed canary grass *Phalaris arundinacea* and reed sweet-grass *Glyceria maxima* among others. The height at which the nest is constructed depends mainly upon the height and structure of the habitat, but can range from 10 cm above ground within a cock's-foot tussock to over a metre high in common reed. These nests are abandoned by late autumn as vegetation dies back and bad weather beats down the sward, so more sheltered habitats are sought out at ground level. During this period harvest mice will use the runways of other small mammals and build temporary, non-breeding nests in the bases of tussocky grasses. In wetland habitats there is movement away from areas prone to flooding in the winter months and Harris (1979) describes them congregating close to sea walls and dry banks above marshes.

A two year study undertaken in Suffolk indicated that habitat connectivity within the landscape increased the likelihood that harvest mice were present. Harvest mouse nests were frequently found in habitats linked via hedgerows, field margins and streams to the Suffolk river valleys, whereas isolated sites were less likely to support harvest mice, despite the presence of suitable habitat (Meek 2011).

### 3.3.  Status and Distribution

In Great Britain, harvest mice are on the north-western edge of their range. Their distribution (*Fig. 3.5*) tends to be biased towards the south and east and most records lie to the south of a line drawn approximately from South-East Wales to the North York Moors. Populations also occur in Pembrokeshire and the coastal strip of North Wales and Cheshire. There are very few isolated colonies in Northumberland, Durham and near Edinburgh. It has been suggested that harvest mouse distribution may be governed by the amount of summer rainfall, but this is likely to be an over-simplification (Harris 1979).

Historically, harvest mice were often encountered in cereal ricks at threshing time, where they had sought cover during the winter months. Changes in agricultural practices, particularly since the introduction of combine harvesters in the 1950s, meant that harvest mice were seen less frequently and consequently it was thought that they may be becoming scarcer. A national survey undertaken in 1970–1975, based on finding nests, found them to be widely distributed and locally common. However, when this was repeated in 1996–1997, populations were found only at 29 % of the original 800 positive sites (Battersby 2005). In contrast, a study which investigated changes in the food of the barn owl between 1974 and 1997 found a large increase in the proportion of harvest mice in

*Figure 3.2.* **Adult harvest mice have golden-russet fur with a white belly.**
Compared with other mice, their muzzle appears blunt and they have small, hairy ears. Their tails are prehensile to aid climbing.
[Pat Morris].

*Figure 3.3.* **Good harvest mouse habitat.**
Left: habitat created after construction of a reservoir. Right: rough field margins and riparian fringes (which also provide connectivity between habitats).
[Mike Ewart; Martha Meek].

the diet in the 1997 survey from negligible numbers to 1.1 % of the prey items.

Harvest mice are considered to be a declining species, so they were added to the list of UK BAP species in the review of 2007. However, this species is unobtrusive and easily overlooked, so its status is difficult to quantify without concentrated field-based effort and it is probably under-recorded in many areas. During the re-survey of 1996–1997, 50 % of sites in Essex were positive and subsequent surveys have found evidence in 20 % of all tetrads in this county (Dobson 1999). A recent study in Suffolk has found evidence of harvest mice in 35 % (80 sites) of 226 samples of owl pellets collected across the county. Subsequent searches for nests confirmed the presence of harvest mouse at 85 % of these locations (45 out of 53 sites) where they had also appeared in an owl pellet. However, nest searches (Meek 2011) have also found nests at 74 % of sites where there had been no evidence of harvest mice in the pellets (31 out of 42 sites). It therefore appears that harvest mice are widespread within these two East Anglian counties.

## 3.4. Legislative Protection

Harvest mice have no specific legal protection under UK or European wildlife legislation. They are, however, a species 'of principal importance for the purpose of conserving biodiversity' covered under Section 41 (England) and Section 42 (Wales) of the Natural Environment and Rural Communities Act (2006) which requires all public bodies to have regard for biodiversity conservation. Harvest mice therefore need to be taken into consideration by a public body when performing any of its functions with a view to conserving biodiversity.

## 3.5. Summary of UK BAP Status and Recommended Actions

The harvest mouse is on the Biodiversity Lists for England and Wales (listed as a Species of Principal Importance under the NERC Act, 2006).

The BAP recommended actions for the harvest mouse are (http://www.jncc.gov.uk/_speciespages/2428.pdf):

- develop a surveillance and monitoring scheme to assess changes in distribution and population trends over time;

- create links on a landscape scale (e.g. hedgerows, fenced river banks) to enable harvest mice to colonise new areas of suitable habitat as they become available;

- ensure that important habitats, such as conservation headlands and buffer strips in Entry Level Stewardship agri-environment schemes, are maintained in the long term in order to create stable, core populations of harvest mice.

**Figure 3.4.** Harvest mouse nest in common reed. [Martha Meek].

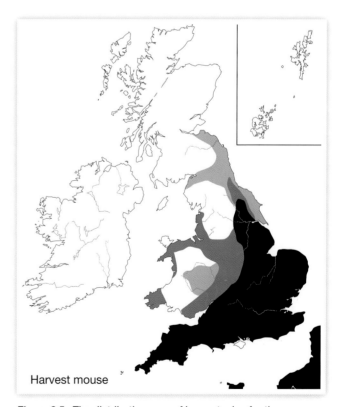

**Figure 3.5.** The distribution map of harvest mice for the British Isles.

Black indicates regular or usual range; dark grey, scattered but regular occurrence; light grey, rare occurrences, vagrants, or scarce and beyond the regular range.

[from: Harris & Yalden (2008) *Mammals of the British Isles: Handbook*, 4th edition. Mammal Society; with minor amendments].

## 3.6.  Survey Methodology

### Establishing the presence of harvest mice

The characteristic woven nest (**Fig. 3.4**) of the harvest mouse is a reliable field sign.  Several county Wildlife Trusts and mammal groups have carried out surveys of their local areas and may be a good source of desk study records.

Non-breeding nests can be constructed all year round, whereas the larger breeding nests (8–10 cm diameter) are constructed only by the female prior to the arrival of each successive litter.  The mouse splits the living leaves of adjacent grasses into a series of narrow strips which are then woven to create a framework for the nest.  More stripped green leaves, still attached to their stems, are then pulled through the nest wall to thicken it.  The nest is therefore firmly attached and supported by the stems of chosen nesting material.  In a freshly constructed breeding nest there is often no obvious entrance hole, so the mother squeezes through the nest wall in one or two locations to gain entry.  The

mother abandons her young when they are 15–16 days old, but they may continue to use the nest for a few more days.  The nest becomes increasingly battered-looking and may have several obvious entrance holes.  Smaller, non-breeding nests, made by males or juveniles often have a distinct single entrance hole.

The height of the nest above ground is dependent upon the type of vegetation used for construction.  In tussocky grasses such as cock's-foot, nests can be found by searching within the base of the tussock.  In taller, stiff-stemmed grasses such as reed canary grass and common reed an aerial nest is constructed at least half way up the flowering stem.  Low-down nests can persist for over a year but nests in reedbeds are normally destroyed during early winter during the first patches of bad weather.

Harvest mice may selectively choose nesting locations where grasses grow up into and are supported by young scrub in grassland, or where the grasses are supported by an adjacent

*Figure 3.6.* Searching vegetation for harvest mouse nests.
[Suffolk Wildlife Trust].

hedgerow. Similarly, they may nest in grasses adjoining bramble patches for the same reason. Surveyors report finding harvest mice in vegetation fringing ponds, particularly if there is a lack of other suitable habitat in the vicinity.

The surveyor will need to check the vegetation closely and thoroughly in order to detect nests as they are never visible without searching (**Fig. 3.6**). For example surveyors should look inside clumps of cock's-foot and other vegetation. In winter, flopped-over vegetation will need to be lifted and parted, so periods when the ground is frozen or snow-covered are unsuitable for surveys. Field voles can also make round nests from shredded grass underneath flopped-over tussocks, but these do not appear woven and they are situated at ground level, rather than within the tussock itself.

Using a transect for nest searching is the most frequently used method, although this may be constrained by the habitat type. Ideally a 200 m transect should be used, to ensure that nests are not missed (J. Dobson, *pers. comm.*). A continuous, uninterrupted search should be made along the transect, within a 2 m wide strip, and this should take approximately one hour for an experienced surveyor. The locations of any nests should be recorded using a GPS device but if no nests are found after a thorough search of potentially suitable habitat, it may be inferred that harvest mice are unlikely to be present within that area. However, depending on the size of the survey area and the complexity of the habitats, more than one transect may need to be undertaken. For example, if riparian habitat borders farmland where there are also field margins or rough grassland, then one transect should encompass the linear wetland habitat and another the farmland habitats.

Within some wetland habitats it may be extremely difficult to use transects, due to the nature of the vegetation and the water level, so searching along the margins of a reedbed, for example, may provide an alternative solution.

Occasionally suitable habitat is found only in small patches within a site. In this case several short searches should be carried out rather than a long transect. In these situations, choosing to search in thick, dense patches of vegetation where grasses dominate will be more productive. A method similar to that employed for searches for hazelnuts opened by dormice could be used. A 10 m x 10 m square can be roughly estimated to encompass one of the most suitable-looking patches, within which the search will take place. After 20 minutes, if no harvest mouse nest is found, move on to another patch and repeat. After five such searches without any evidence of harvest mice, the likelihood of them being present will be low.

Other methods for recording presence/absence of harvest mice include Longworth live trapping and bait tube sampling. Live trapping is much more labour intensive and requires the use of specialist equipment. It is most likely to be successful during the winter months when harvest mice are more terrestrial, but coincides with the period when populations are at their lowest. Collection of droppings from bait tubes for DNA analysis is expensive and has not been proven to be cost-effective. The Mammal Society pilot study of 2009 found that nest searching appeared to give more positive results than trapping or bait tubes. Nest searching should therefore be the preferred survey method.

Owl pellet analysis has also been employed to detect harvest mice. In Suffolk this method has been used to determine broad locations for harvest mouse presence within the barn owl's hunting range, thus directing surveyors to locations where nest searching is likely to be most profitable. However, in a site-specific study, looking for nests would still be the most efficient way of locating harvest mice. This study has shown that there appears to be an increased likelihood of quickly finding harvest mice where the habitat is linked to other suitable habitat, such as river estuaries or grazing marsh (Meek 2011).

### Estimating population size

Harvest mice are unobtrusive mammals so it is difficult to obtain a reliable estimate of population size and there is also a large seasonal variation in their numbers. No general relationship has yet been identified which predicts population abundance from nest counts (Riordan et al. 2009). Earlier studies have demonstrated that the higher the nest density, the more harvest mice are actually captured (Trout 1978), so there is likely to be some link between numbers of animals and the number of nests, with a greater number of mice resulting in the building of a higher number of nests. It is therefore possible that a count of the number of nests found during a survey may be a simple way of gauging the relative size of the population. Recording the time it takes to find each nest and the times thereafter for subsequent nests may also be useful in predicting abundance.

Recording the number of breeding nests gives an indirect method of estimating the birth rate (natality) and therefore the annual recruitment to the population, assuming a mean litter size of 5.3 young.

However, this information can be difficult to interpret in practice. In a study employing nearly one hundred 200 m transects within three counties, the frequency of nests on each 'positive' transect tended to be low at only one or two nests (Riordan et al. 2009).

Similarly, researchers in East Anglia frequently find fewer than four nests when searching a similar distance (Meek, *pers. comm.*; Dobson, J., *pers. comm.*). In such situations it is hard to draw conclusions about population size.

### Survey timing

Towards the end of the breeding season, harvest mouse nests will be at their most numerous and from this time onwards through the winter they are also more visible, standing out as withered, grassy balls. Surveys for nests are therefore most productive when undertaken during October–March. Surveys in wetland areas should be carried out in autumn if possible, as nests in reedbeds are often destroyed by bad weather over winter.

Occasionally from October to December, nests may still be occupied by late litters if the weather is good so these should not be removed or excessively disturbed. The die back of vegetation in autumn is also variable, depending on the weather conditions, so the vegetation may not have died back at all making searching time-consuming.

Longworth trapping studies are likely to be most successful during the winter, when vegetation dies back and harvest mice are living almost exclusively at ground level. Longworth traps can be deployed during the summer by fixing to stakes within the stalk zone of tall grasses, but again, this is labour-intensive and is likely to yield limited results.

## 3.7. Impact Assessment, Mitigation, Compensation and Enhancement

It is not straightforward to assess the impacts of a project on harvest mice in any robust way. As explained above, it is difficult to obtain any reliable estimate of population size, and hence to formally assess the geographical importance of the population or, therefore, the significance of the effect in population terms. In parts of the south and east, such as East Anglia, where harvest mice exist at carrying capacity in good, well-connected habitat, development projects may not have a significant effect on the local population. Where significant effects are predicted these are likely to be significant at, for example, the County or Local level. However, if a large-scale development were to affect an isolated population identified at the edge of, or outside of, their known range, significant effects would be more likely to occur, and the effects could be significant at National or Regional levels.

Mitigation for local effects should be possible through good practice in site clearance, habitat creation and management, and these issues are discussed below.

### Habitat loss and fragmentation

Harvest mice are likely to be encountered during surveys for project proposals on greenfield land where there is a grassy sward, although they are very unlikely to be present in grass that has been cut in the last two years. Wetland habitats such as reedbeds, grazing marsh and fens have a particularly high likelihood of supporting harvest mice. Other potential habitat may include former airfields, arable land in 'set aside', field margins on recently farmed arable land, pasture, rough grassland and any habitats bordering water such as the edges of drainage ditches, dykes, ponds or riverbanks. Where large-scale projects such as residential or mixed-use developments are to be located in farmland, this could lead to loss of harvest mouse habitat or an interruption to their ability to move within the landscape.

Harvest mice are a fairly mobile species and often occupy ephemeral habitats which can change quite rapidly within months or even a few years. Seasonal changes and winter flooding can result in short-term movements, as can other activities such as agricultural practices, including rotational cutting of field margins. They are therefore well adapted to being a transitory species, moving back into areas as the habitat becomes more suitable. However, fragmentation of the countryside, such as loss of hedgerows and field margins, draining of wetlands and loss of riparian habitat will interrupt their ability to recolonise sites, even when the habitat is suitable.

Development that seeks to reduce these effects will benefit harvest mice, as well as a range of other species.

Major infrastructure projects, such as new road schemes, can also result in isolation of habitats and while culverts might allow for the passage of larger, more mobile animals, they are less likely to be used by harvest mice unless there is a dry passage with some cover. Roadside embankments can provide suitable habitat if they are allowed to develop a grassy sward and the presence of scattered scrub is also not detrimental to the presence of harvest mice as long as it does not become dominant.

Large flood relief schemes or watercourse diversion projects may cause loss of habitat, but creation of new habitat will benefit harvest mice, particularly if there are opportunities for natural recolonisation. It is likely that mitigation for other species protected by UK and European legislation will be the principal drivers behind any such mitigation scheme, but opportunities should also be taken to consider harvest mice within the overall project design.

The creation of new habitat, which may be required to mitigate effects upon protected species such as water vole, has the potential to provide opportunities for harvest mice as well. Habitat creation for harvest mice is a relatively straightforward process and as long as there is a well-connected 'reservoir' population nearby, new areas should be colonised quite rapidly.

### Incidental mortality due to projects

Clearance of small areas of vegetation during late autumn will have less impact upon harvest mice, but the position of the site within the landscape should be considered and whether there is other suitable habitat to which the population can retreat for winter cover. Vegetation removal in late winter/ early spring is likely to have the greatest impact as populations will be at their lowest and this period should be avoided, along with the breeding season.

Vegetation clearance should be undertaken in a series of successive strips up to 6 m wide, working towards the direction of the refuge area. If reptiles are present and the mitigation plan is that they are to be encouraged into neighbouring habitat (rather than captured and translocated), then vegetation manipulation for this group will be applicable to harvest mice also.

Where remaining populations would be unviable, or large sites will be affected, then translocation will be necessary. This is only feasible using a Longworth live trapping programme. While captures are more likely to be higher in winter, so will be the mortality of re-released animals into the receptor area. An autumn trapping and translocation programme avoids the breeding season and should have greatest rates of survival. Translocation in April, prior to the breeding season, could be considered if there is no alternative, but as the species does well in captivity, it may be possible to trap in autumn and release in the spring. Ideally the receptor site should be close to the original population, but should not have an existing population of harvest mice (as determined by a survey). The habitat should already be suitable for harvest mice as it is difficult to 'enhance' an unsuitable habitat for this species in the short term. If the receptor site is poorly connected to other suitable habitats which might contain harvest mouse populations, then consideration should be given to improving these linkages as part of the mitigation process.

### Mitigation for habitat loss

Given 2–3 years, good habitat for harvest mice is easily creatable. Former arable land or areas of bare ground can be allowed to develop rough grassland and this will also benefit a variety of farmland birds and other species such as reptiles. This habitat can develop through natural regeneration or by sowing a grassland mix that includes cock's-foot. The size of the area to be created can range from linear field margins to whole fields. Where public access is allowed, use of paths should be encouraged and areas should be protected from excessive trampling. In schemes involving the planting of new hedgerows, this will

only benefit harvest mice if there is a grassy margin allowed to develop adjacent to the hedgerow. In Suffolk, wild bird cover mixes containing varieties of millet have been found to support higher than average densities of harvest mouse nests. This could provide a useful short-term enhancement to their habitat while permanent grassland is becoming established.

When considering future management, cutting should always be rotational to retain blocks of good habitat. Ideally, each area should be cut on a four or even five year rotation and certainly no more frequently than every three years. Many habitats that are allowed to develop into tussocky grassland require minimal intervention, such as some annual scrub removal.

The creation of reed beds in conjunction with new water bodies will also provide new habitat for harvest mice as well as a host of other species and requires minimal long-term management as long as the water levels are maintained at a high enough level.

## 3.8. Research Requirements

Key research requirements include:

- how far can harvest mice disperse if their habitat is cut down?
- what are the barriers to dispersal? Do they cross roads and what size of road becomes a barrier?
- how resilient to habitat loss are they?
- how far do harvest mice disperse within different habitat types?
- a method is needed to predict harvest mouse abundance from nest counts.

## 3.9. References and Bibliography

Battersby, J. (ed.) (2005) *UK Mammals: Species Status and Population Trends*. First Report by the Tracking Mammals Partnership. JNCC, Peterborough.

Dobson, J. (1999) *The Mammals of Essex*. Lopinga Books, Saffron Walden, Essex.

Harris, S. (1979) *Secret Life of the Harvest Mouse*. Hamlyn. London.

Love, R. A., Webbon, C., Glue, D. E. & Harris, S. (2000) Changes in the food of British barn owls (*Tyto alba*) between 1974 and 1997. *Mammal Review* **30**: 107–129.

Meek, M. (2011) Suffolk's Harvest Mice in Focus. Report by Suffolk Wildlife Trust to the People's Trust for Endangered Species.

Perrow, M. R. & Jowitt, A.J.D. (1995) What future for the harvest mouse? *British Wildlife* **6**: 356–365.

Price, C. R. (2003) Late Pleistocene and Early Holocene Small Mammals in South West Britain. *BAR British Series* **347** Oxford.

Riordan, P., Lloyd, A. & Macdonald, D.W. (2009) *Do harvest mouse nest survey results predict population size?* Report to People's Trust for Endangered Species.

Trout, R. C. (1978) A review of studies on populations of wild harvest mice (*Micromys minutus*, Pallas). *Mammal Review* **8**: 143–158.

Woods, M., Mcdonald, R. A. & Harris, S. (2003) Predation of wildlife by domestic cats *Felis catus* in Great Britain. *Mammal Review* **33**: 174–188.

## Acknowledgements

*The author would like to thank Martha Meek of Suffolk Wildlife Trust for her advice and constructive comments.*

# Brown Hare and Mountain Hare

*Figure 4.1.* **Brown and mountain hare.**
Above: brown hare and below: mountain hare, in summer (left) and winter (right) coats.
[Christine Gregory; Davide D'Acunto; Silviu Petrovan].

## 4. Brown Hare and Mountain Hare

*By Phil Wheeler, Stephanie Wray and Derek Yalden*

### 4.1. Background Biology

Much of the information in this section is taken from summaries in Harris & Yalden (2008).

Hares *Lepus* spp., along with rabbits, are members of the family Leporidae. There are two confirmed species in the British Isles (*Fig. 4.1*) and possibly three depending upon taxonomic judgement. These are the brown hare, the mountain hare and the Irish hare.

The brown hare *Lepus europaeus* is the largest and most abundant. It is widespread in the lowlands of mainland Britain, especially in farmland habitats. Averaging about 55 cm in body length and 3.5 kg in weight, brown hares are characteristically reddish-brown with long (10 cm) ears that have big black patches on the back surface of the tip. The mountain hare *Lepus timidus* is found especially on moorlands in Scotland, but also in the Peak District of England and on the Isle of Man. It is slightly smaller than the brown hare, averaging about 50 cm in body length and 2.7 kg in weight. It is variable in colour, but is usually a greyish-brown, sometimes very grey (hence one of its common names, the 'blue hare') but sometimes sandy-brown. Its ears are shorter than the brown hare (about 7 cm, the same as a rabbit) and with only a thin black rim. The tail is usually an all-white powder-puff (whereas brown hares, like rabbits, have black-topped tails). Distinctively, the mountain hare turns white in winter (*Fig. 4.1*).

The Irish hare *Lepus timidus hibernicus* is a distinctive type of the mountain hare, genetically rather different from the Scottish mountain hare, and possibly to be regarded as a full species *Lepus hibernicus*. It is usually sandy-brown, with the same white powder-puff of a tail, but does not turn white in winter. It is slightly larger than the Scottish form (on average, 54 cm body length, 3.4 kg in weight). It is not confined to moorlands, but is the common lowland and farmland hare in Ireland where it occupies the niche of the brown hare (Harris & Yalden 2008).

Hares are generally animals of open country, sitting tight in a shallow depression (known as a form) and relying on their camouflage to escape notice if possible, using their long hind limbs to run away from danger when discovered. Their large eyes, situated high on the head, give them all-round vision when in the form. The ears are kept flat along the back when the hare is resting, and when it is trying to escape unnoticed. When active and feeding, the ears are raised, and are then effective at hearing approaching danger. The sense of smell is also acute.

Hares are herbivorous, feeding on a range of grasses, herbs and dwarf shrubs. The most nutritious fresh growth is favoured during the breeding season, but bark, twigs and other poorer food may be eaten in winter when fresh growth is unavailable. Food passes through the gut twice. During the daytime, at rest in its form, the hare produces soft pellets which are eaten directly from the anus. At night, when the hare is feeding, the soft pellets pass through the gut again, and are ejected as the familiar hard, round pellets.

Hares are usually solitary animals, though several may gather in loose parties in suitable places when food or cover is good. They are generally nocturnal, and occupy a home range which is surprisingly small given their mobility.

For brown hares, annual ranges might be 20–190 ha, yet they may commute 1.7 km between feeding sites and resting sites (Harris & Yalden 2008). The size and use of the home range changes during the day and between the seasons, as patches of feeding and sheltering habitat become more or less suitable. Night-time ranges are typically 50 % larger than daytime ranges. For Irish hares, home range size may vary between a tiny 14 ha on improved reseed, to more typical 40–50 ha. In Scotland, on moorland habitat, mountain hare home ranges may extend up to 113 ha. Mountain hares may move long distances, 15 km or more, if deep snow cover forces them to leave their moorland habitat (Harris & Yalden 2008). Dispersal (i.e. permanent movement to a new area) by both brown and mountain hares is surprisingly short. While some individuals do disperse long distances, sometimes several kilometres, most disperse distances no more than a few hundred metres from their natural range.

Under good conditions, females of both species of hare can breed over an 8 month period, from February through to August, September or even later (Harris & Yalden 2008). Typically the mountain hare breeding season in Scotland is shorter (between 1st March and 31st July) and this is the close season enshrined in the 2011 Wildlife and Natural Heritage (Scotland) Act. Mating can occur from January through to August. Despite the popular myth, March is not especially significant and it may be that mad March hares are more apparent because vegetation is shorter and hare behaviour is easier to see at that time of year. Females produce typically 3 litters (up to 5) in a season, of 1–4 young known as leverets (Harris & Yalden 2008). Early and late litters tend to be smaller, as are litters produced by younger females.

UK BAP MAMMALS: Interim Guidance for Survey Methodologies, Impact Assessment and Mitigation    Brown Hare and Mountain Hare

Brown Hare and Mountain Hare

*Figure 4.2.* **Hare habitat.**
Above: brown hare in arable habitat.  Below: on moorland, the mix of young nutritious heather that has been recently burnt and senescent heather gives cover provides optimum conditions for mountain hares.
[Silviu Petrovan; Derek Yalden].

*Figure 4.3.* **Hare forms.**
A brown hare form (upper left), and a mountain hare form (bottom left). A brown hare in a form (right).
[Derek Yalden; Christine Gregory].

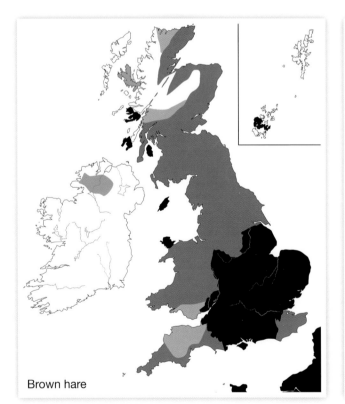

Brown hare

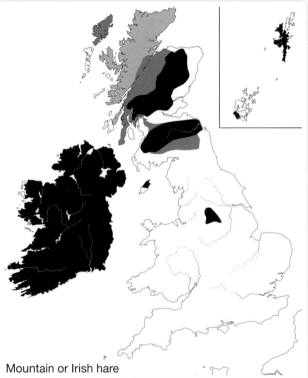

Mountain or Irish hare

*Figure 4.4.* **The distribution map of brown (left) and mountain hares (right) for the British Isles.**
Black indicates regular or usual range; dark grey, scattered but regular occurrence; light grey, rare occurrences, vagrants, or scarce and beyond the regular range. Note that brown hares are also known to be abundant on the Isle of Tiree. Their range shown in the north-east part of the mainland may be misleading in places, particularly around the fringes surrounding the main upland areas (e.g. Cairngorms/Grampians), where there is overlap with mountain hares (Rob Raynor, *pers. comm.*).
[from: Harris & Yalden (2008) *Mammals of the British Isles: Handbook,* 4th edition. Mammal Society; with minor amendments].

UK BAP MAMMALS: Interim Guidance for Survey Methodologies, Impact Assessment and Mitigation    Brown Hare and Mountain Hare

Brown Hare and Mountain Hare

Leverets are born fully furred, with open eyes and ears; for the first day or two, they rest together in a form, but then separate to individual forms. Their mother comes to suckle them once a day, for about 5 minutes only, in the evening. They are independent after about 4 weeks, by which time their mother is about to give birth again.

## 4.2. Habitat Requirements

Hares live mostly in open habitats (*Fig. 4.2*), are usually only found at low density in extensive woodlands, and cope poorly with urban and suburban habitats. They require a suitable sequence of food sources to see them through the year, and similarly a range of suitable cover types.

On farmland, brown and Irish hares are highly dependent on the agricultural cycle. Ideally, a sequence offered by spring-sown cereals with a weed-rich undergrowth, hay meadows or pasture in summer, autumn aftermath and winter stubble would provide food through the year. Field margins and beetle banks provide good food sources and cover in fields that are otherwise tightly harvested or mown. In winter, woodland may provide shelter in otherwise exposed landscapes. Hares move round these habitats during the year, grazing in young silage or cereal fields but moving out when stock, especially sheep, are released onto pasture in early summer. A landscape with a mixture of arable crops, hayfields and pasture, divided by hedges with field margins, offers hares the chance to move round these habitats during the annual cycle. Conversely, large, prairie-like fields of single crops, with few hedges or margins, or large grass fields with herds of sheep or cattle competing for food and destroying potential cover, restrict or remove these options.

On moorland, the mix of young nutritious heather that has been recently burnt and old or senescent heather providing cover which gamekeepers produce to support the grouse population appears to provide optimum conditions for mountain hares, although they also utilise woodland including young conifer plantations (Harris & Yalden 2008). The form (*Fig. 4.3*) is important to the hare's survival during the daytime. Typically it will be beside a tuft of grass or rushes, offering a view at least in front. In open fields, it may be a shallow scrape in the soil, enough to cover the lower half of the body but leaving the top of the head and back just visible. A site on a gentle slope may be favoured, again offering a good view over the open ground in front. On moorland, forms might be in deep heather or moor-grass, but are often in the shelter of rocks, on steep slopes with, again, a good view down-slope. Mountain hares respond to weather, often moving to shelter on the leeward side of a slope, or sunbathing in the winter sun on south-facing rocks.

The most critical forms are those needed by the leverets, especially during their first few days when they are very vulnerable. Because leverets can be born at any time from February to September for the brown hare and Irish hare, and typically March to July for the mountain hare, the suitability of the surrounding countryside varies. Moorland usually has an adequate supply of deep heather, whatever the season, and it is the poor nutritional value of the available diet in winter that limits growth (Harris & Yalden 2008). The dramatic changes in farmland during the agricultural year pose challenges for brown and Irish hares. Growing hay or silage crops are nutritious and deep enough to provide good shelter. Mechanical harvesting, however, and the early and multiple silage cuts (2–3 in a summer) in particular, are suspected to be a major problem. Hares, especially leverets, are likely to be killed by mowers, as corncrakes certainly are, but evidence is scant.

## 4.3. Status and Distribution

The brown hare used to be common and widespread throughout lowland Britain, as did the Irish hare in Ireland. Various lines of evidence indicate that they have become much more patchily distributed, and less abundant where they still occur (*Fig. 4.4*) (Hutchings & Harris 1996). The reasons for this decline are not fully understood, and although it is believed to be primarily related to agricultural intensification, other factors such as predation, disease and shooting effort may have some influence. Some of the best data come from game bags, which show a reduction in average bags from 12 $km^{-2}$ in 1961 to 2 $km^{-2}$ in 1990; these data come from some of the best managed game estates, where hares are flourishing (Tapper 1992). The national distribution surveys carried out in the 1990s show that numbers are still high, around 40 $km^{-2}$, in the agricultural counties of eastern England, but that the three counties of Cambridgeshire, Norfolk and Suffolk (only 5 % of the land area of Britain) hosted 20 % of the brown hare population. Conversely, hares were vanishingly few in the far western counties of Cornwall and Devon, as well as in much of Wales, where historical records show that they used to be common. The national population, in spring, was estimated to be around 800,000 in surveys both in 1991–1993 and 1996–1997.

Mountain hares are particularly variable in numbers from year to year. Often, there is a ten-year cycle of abundance, so that game bags vary between 2 and 16 $km^{-2}$. This makes it difficult to suggest a sensible overall population estimate; a figure of 350,000 has been cautiously suggested by Harris *et al.* 1995. Numbers are highest on the moors of north-east Scotland, where there may be between

Brown Hare and Mountain Hare

Brown Hare and Mountain Hare UK BAP MAMMALS: Interim Guidance for Survey Methodologies, Impact Assessment and Mitigation

50–200 km$^{-2}$, and lowest on the wet acidic moors of north-west Scotland, where there may only be 2–5 km$^{-2}$ (Harris & Yalden 2008).

Distribution surveys in 1995–1996, repeated in 2006–2007 (Kinrade *et al*. 2008), suggest that mountain hares are present in about half the upland area of Scotland (away from the central belt), and that there has been no significant change in range (and hence probably numbers) recently, although there is anecdotal evidence of very heavy localised culling on some Highland estates for the purpose of tick reduction. If the population estimate of 350,000 is correct, the total bag for both game and pest control is only about 7 % of the population.

The English population showed three serious fluctuations, more than tenfold, between 1970 and 2000, but has remained steady, at a high level, in the last decade. An overall estimate of the Peak District population, based on known distribution (Mallon 2001) and distance sampling along 280 km of line transect, suggests a healthy population of around 10,000 (Mallon *et al*. 2003).

The Irish hare still has a wide distribution across Ireland, but declined tenfold between 1914 and 1960, according to game bags (Reid *et al*. 2007). Road-transect surveys in 2007 suggested a total population of 649,000, and various surveys suggest densities across the decade varying from 1–5 km$^{-2}$, in line with known cycles of abundance (Reid *et al*. 2007). The brown hare has been repeatedly introduced to Ireland, for sporting purposes, but has established only a limited range and abundance, in the north-east (Reid *et al*. 2007).

## 4.4. Legislative Protection

Hares have limited legal protection throughout most of the British Isles; they remain game species and can be serious pests of forestry and agriculture where numbers become too high. Legislation prohibits certain methods of taking or killing of mountain hares; in Scotland under Schedule 3 of the Conservation (Natural Habitats, &c.) Regulations 1994, and in England under Schedule 4 of the Conservation of Habitats and Species Regulations (2010 ). The Hare Preservation Act 1892, provides limited protection by forbidding the sale of adult brown hares or leverets during their main breeding period. This is specified in the Act as being between 1$^{st}$ March–31$^{st}$ July. Hares are also covered by the Game Act 1831 and the Ground Game Act 1880. As a consequence of EC legislation, (Annex V of the EC Habitats Directive (1992)) the mountain hare is a species 'of community interest whose taking in the wild and exploitation may be subject to management measures'. It is a requirement of this legislation that the sustainability of the harvest is assured,

requiring that population and harvest levels are monitored. Irish hares have some legal protection, particularly to regulate the manner in which hare coursing is undertaken.

## 4.5. Summary of UK BAP Status and Recommended Actions

Because of the obvious declines in abundance and distribution of hares, especially brown and Irish hares, both species are on the UK Biodiversity Action Plan as a priority species for conservation.

The brown hare is on the Biodiversity Lists for England and Wales (listed as a Species of Principal Importance under the NERC Act, 2006), and Scotland (under the Nature Conservation (Scotland) Act 2004). Brown hares were on the original 1994 list, with a target of doubling brown hare numbers by 2010, from 0.8 to 1.6 million. An average density of 10 km$^{-2}$ across the country would achieve this, and since numbers have been shown to respond quickly to habitat improvements, this was a realistic target. It is not certain that it has been met, but available evidence suggests some success.

The BAP recommended actions for the brown hare are (http://jncc.defra.gov.uk/_speciespages/410.pdf):

- encourage appropriate habitat management in pastoral and arable areas (e.g. field margins, beetle banks, overwinter stubble, ungrazed waterside and hedge strips, hay meadows and late mowing) through uptake of Entry and Higher Level agri-environment schemes;

- enhancement of effort in surveillance schemes to ensure population trends can be determined, particularly at the regional level;

- CAP reform to ensure adequate conservation measures available to benefit brown hare.

The mountain hare was listed on the UK BAP in 2007 and is on the Biodiversity Lists for England (listed as a Species of Principal Importance under the NERC Act 2006), and Scotland (under the Nature Conservation (Scotland) Act 2004).

The BAP objectives for the mountain hare are (http://jncc.defra.gov.uk/_speciespages/2379.pdf):

- update the available information on the distribution of mountain/Irish hares in Scotland and Northern Ireland by appropriate survey; develop and validate a practical and cost-effective survey and monitoring methodology for mountain hares in Scotland;

- work with Scottish Land & Estates (formerly the Scottish Rural Property and Business Association), Ulster Farmers' Union, Game Conservancy Trust and the Moorland Forum to agree best practice guidelines for hare

UK BAP MAMMALS: Interim Guidance for Survey Methodologies, Impact Assessment and Mitigation    Brown Hare and Mountain Hare

Brown Hare and Mountain Hare

*Figure 4.5.* Hare and rabbit droppings for comparison.
[Derek Yalden].

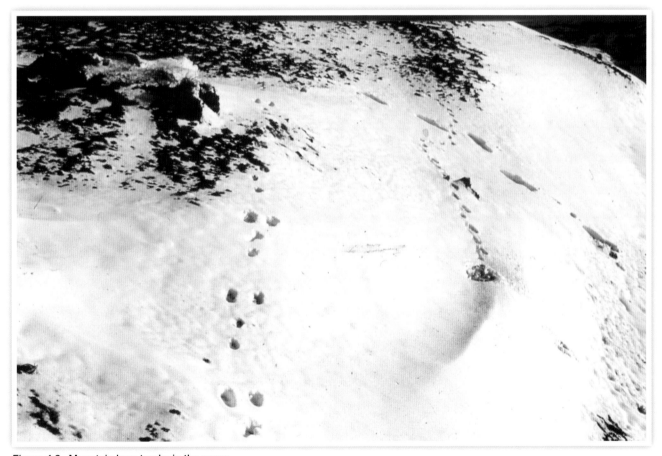

*Figure 4.6.* Mountain hare tracks in the snow.
[Derek Yalden].

Brown Hare and Mountain Hare

Brown Hare and Mountain Hare      UK BAP MAMMALS: Interim Guidance for Survey Methodologies, Impact Assessment and Mitigation

management which do not threaten local populations; publicise the guidelines and encourage their widespread adoption;

- investigate the effects of exploitation on hare populations and their dynamics;

- investigate how current land use changes and the influence of climate change are likely to affect mountain/Irish hare populations in the long term, through changes in their habitat;

- continue to monitor the mountain hare population in northern England;

- subject to the success of the above actions, review the legal status of the mountain hare.

## 4.6. Survey Methodology

A range of different methodologies are available to survey hares and different techniques will be appropriate depending upon the questions to be answered. See also Newey *et al.* (2008) which critically reviews the methods applicable to mountain hares.

### Desk studies

Before commencing any field survey, it may be appropriate to collate known records of the presence of hares. Potential sources of information include the National Biodiversity Network, local records centres and the Game & Wildlife Conservation Trust. Local distribution surveys and county records offices can usually report the likelihood of their presence in a particular 1 km$^2$ or 10 km$^2$ and, with such wide-ranging animals, this might be sufficient. Thus, a desk study may establish the presence of hares in an area of interest with sufficient reliability to make it unnecessary to undertake a field survey. Since hares are such widespread species within their national ranges, absence from regional data or published distribution maps cannot be assumed to represent real absence from an area; hares may be present but at low densities.

### Establishing the presence of hares

Depending upon the reasons for the survey (for example, in cases where enhancements are proposed) it may be appropriate to undertake a survey to confirm the presence of hares on a particular moorland or farm. This can be done through searches for field signs (mainly droppings *Fig. 4.5*) or through visual searches, which are best undertaken just before dusk or just after dawn. Changes in hare behaviour during the seasons and their large home ranges will make reliable presence/absence difficult to ascertain except over very large search areas.

Given their vulnerability to road traffic collisions, roadside carcasses are a frequent way of detecting hares. Most landowners and naturalists are familiar

with the animals, and simple questionnaire surveys are an efficient way of confirming their presence on any particular land-holding. The most characteristic field signs of hares are droppings. Hard round or slightly flattened pellets, about 1 cm across, are a characteristic sign of their presence, and their feeding sites. The pellets are usually straw-coloured to mid-brown, though they can be black, like rabbit pellets, when hares have been grazing on young cereal or grass leaves. Rabbit droppings are often left in big piles, because rabbit colonies are territorial and the males use droppings as markers; moreover they are often associated with their scrapes and burrows. By contrast, hare droppings are usually scattered around singly or in small groups, though they can be associated with temporary resting sites, such as posts or small bushes. Hares, particularly mountain hares, sometimes produce obvious trails through longer vegetation, especially when commuting between regular feeding areas and resting sites. The footprints are characteristic in snow: long (15 cm) paired 'dashes' left by the hind feet, usually just ahead of the staggered 'dots' of the front feet (*Fig. 4.6*). Only the much smaller rabbit tracks (8 cm hind feet) tracks are similar. Because their feet are fully furred, hares and rabbits do not show the individual pads characteristic of rodent or carnivore tracks, but the four claws sometimes produce quite a fox-like hind footprint when a hare is running on its toes.

Other than droppings, hare signs are subtle. On moorland, trails running along the side of regularly used eroded channels (groughs) in peat, as well as paths through tall heather or other long vegetation, may show regular commuting routes but these may be difficult to attribute to species. On farmland, too, trails on ploughed farmland may reveal regular highways. Fur is sometimes left on barbed wire, or as a result of 'boxing matches', especially during the spring moult. When a hare is flushed from its form, the form is often a very obvious depression in the soil or cup in the vegetation, sometimes (during moult) with a slight lining of fur. However, none of these signs is sufficiently obvious, regularly distributed or reliably observed to be useful for monitoring purposes.

An assessment of the general habitat will, however, reveal obvious areas of value. In an otherwise extensive crop, small headlands, field margins and banks may provide good lying-up sites as well as better feeding sites. Small copses and field-corner woodlands may be similarly important. On bald limestone plateaux, the less managed and floristically richer dale-sides are likely to be important for both species. A small area of rushes or longer grass in an otherwise tightly grazed pasture may provide important cover. Anything that adds diversity in an otherwise monotonous landscape is likely to be important to hares.

### Quantitative surveys for hares

Where it is important to judge the size of a population, the possible impacts of some projects on it, or demonstrate that some remedial action has been successful, it will be necessary to undertake a more detailed and quantitative survey. The main methods of quantitative survey are line transects, pellet counts and spotlight counts. All of these methods can be used to make an estimate of hare density or hare population. However, due to the relatively low density at which hares live throughout a large proportion of their natural range, these methods can be difficult to apply to small-scale potential development sites. In these cases, it may be necessary to seek access to a wider area for survey purposes.

### Transect surveys

A line transect involves travelling a known distance along some predetermined route, counting the hares seen and estimating their perpendicular distance, when first seen, from that route. The simplest interpretation of this method is to generate an estimate of the area sampled and hence hare density by multiplying the length of the transect by the average perpendicular distance to hare sightings.

Distance sampling uses statistical modelling to estimate the area surveyed and calculate density. The distribution of sighting distances represents the relationship between distance from the observer and probability of detection, the 'detection function', not the distribution of hares since there are still hares at greater distances from the observer but they are less likely to be seen. The 'effective' transect (or 'strip') width is therefore the distance up to which as many hares are missed as are seen beyond. Calculating the detection function involves some moderately sophisticated statistics but this, the effective strip width, population density estimates and population sizes where appropriate can be calculated with a number of types of software, including the program DISTANCE[4] which is freely downloadable. There is a range of books that cover basic and more advanced distance sampling, free online tutorials and training courses in the use of distance software.[5]

Distance sampling has a number of key

assumptions and before undertaking a distance sampling survey it is important to ensure that these can be met:

- hares actually on the transect must be seen with certainty, and this certainty drops off with distance;

- transects are placed randomly with respect to landscape features;

- hares are observed before they move in response to the observer.

Traditionally, hare transect surveys have used human observers walking across likely habitat and, although time-consuming, this appears to be the most reliable method, though some problems in accuracy have been recorded for mountain hares at high density (Newey et al. 2003). The labour intensive nature of this approach can be reduced by employing a well-trained pointing dog quartering a defined beat. In agricultural areas transects on foot are probably best conducted during the winter when crops are either absent from fields or the height of crops or grass is low so hares are more likely to be seen.

The timing of hare surveys is not straightforward. Hares are most active at night (particularly around dawn and dusk) and rest in forms during the day. Petrovan et al. (2011) demonstrated that daytime surveys are much less efficient than night-time ones, and that surveys for hares during the day can fail to detect them even in sites where they are present at moderate densities. Therefore in most cases night-time surveys should be the default option. However, at high hare densities, it may be most practical to survey during the daytime since individuals moving away from an observer at night in high density sites may disturb others without the observer's knowledge. Unless health and safety, time or logistical constraints prevent it, it is recommended to carry out pilot surveys during both day and night-time and base further effort on an assessment of those.

Surveys should not be carried out in fog, heavy rain or under a full moon as hare detectability is much reduced in these conditions. It is important in any survey of hares to ensure that animals are correctly identified and not confused with rabbits. Some observer training in the field is recommended, but there are occasions where identification of animals at a distance will be uncertain. In such cases the animal should be approached slowly to ensure a correct identification.

The Irish hare surveys (Reid et al. 2007) used road transects; that is, a car was driven along a known (predetermined) route, at night, while a pair of observers with strong torches checked the areas either side of the road at five points on each 1 km transect, and estimated the distance from the road of any hares seen. Road transects for

---

[4] Freely downloadable from http://www.ruwpa.st-and.ac.uk/distance/

[5] For instance, courses offered by The Centre for Research into Ecological and Environmental Modelling http://creem2.st-andrews.ac.uk/

distance sampling are not recommended because the method violates some of the key assumptions of distance sampling, namely that transects are randomly placed in the landscape (roads usually are not) and that all animals on or very close to the transects are detected with certainty (often hedgerows mean a strip very close to the transect is not observed). It is also possible that the extra noise generated by a vehicle at night will cause hares to move away from the observer unseen long before the vehicle is within observation distance of the hare. Road transects may be of limited use for detecting the presence (but not absence) of hares, and have the limited merit of allowing much more ground to be surveyed.

### Spotlight counts

A spotlight count requires a known area of field or moorland to be surveyed from a good observation point, when hares are actively feeding, and therefore visible. This is normally done at night-time, using a powerful spotlight, although it is possible to use natural daylight on late summer evenings, when the short nights force hares to start feeding before nightfall. The area is marked out beforehand, using natural or artificial markers, and should ideally be a concave bowl of feeding habitat (Langbein et al. 1999).

Distances to hares can, depending on the terrain, either be estimated by eye after a training period, paced in the field, or preferably measured with a laser rangefinder. Nocturnal surveys should be carried out with a one million candlepower lamp with sufficient battery power to permit three to four hours' surveying. The assumptions and likely degree of error should be stated in any report.

### Estimating hare populations using pellet surveys

Pellet surveys have been widely used in studies of herbivorous mammals (Neff 1968; Putman 1984; Newey et al. 2011). Pellet surveys are usually based on counting the standing crop of faeces at a particular point in time, or on clearing faecal pellets from permanent plots and calculating faecal accumulation rates. The statistical assumptions and potential pitfalls of these two techniques are explored by Mitchell et al. (1977), Putman (1984; 1990) and Staines & Ratcliffe (1987).

The major drawback of using clearance plots is that many plots will accumulate no pellets in the time allowed. This will be a particular problem if population levels are low. Faecal standing crop methods do not suffer from these problems. However, such an approach can only provide a 'snapshot' of the pellet population and takes no account of the dynamic nature of faecal standing crop. If estimates of population density are made using such a technique, then corrections must be

made for differential rates of decomposition, since this will vary widely in different habitats (Wigley & Johnson 1981; Mitchell et al. 1977).

A method which alleviates some of these problems and combines the favourable aspects of standing crop and faecal accumulation methods was developed by Taylor & Williams (1956) working on rabbits in New Zealand. However, it is still important to note that pellet surveys are inherently variable and can usually only be relied upon to give a rank index of relative population size.

The method utilises two estimates of pellet density (M1 and M2) separated by an interval of T days between t1 and t2. At the first survey, M1 is counted, and a proportion (normally 20 – 30 %) of these pellets (k1) is marked. T days later (at time t2) a second estimate of pellet density is made (M2) and the number of marked pellets remaining (k2) is recorded. Since pellet decay is assumed to be an exponential function of the rate at which pellets present at t1 disappear, then pellets may be expected to decay at a rate of $k2/k1 = e^{-c(t2-t1)}$ and those pellets present at t2 will be $M2 = M1k2/k1 + PdQ$, where d is the defaecation rate, Q is the proportion of pellets deposited after t1 which persist intact to t2 and P is the population size.

The population size can therefore be calculated from:

$$P = \frac{(M2 - M1k2/k1)\log_e(k1/k2)}{(1 - k2/k1)dT}$$

Estimates of hare defaecation rates are available in the literature, typically around 100–150 pellets a day, although these vary with factors such as the available browse species, the age structure of the population and the time of year. However, this method resolves some of the potential pitfalls of pellet surveys and can be an effective census technique.

### Survey timing

Hare surveys are typically undertaken in late winter/ early spring, when vegetation cover is lowest and hares are most visible. At this time, few leverets will have weaned and hunting will typically have finished so the count is likely to represent the adult pre-breeding population.

## 4.7. Impact Assessment, Mitigation, Compensation and Enhancement

The main potential effects of projects on hares are:

- increases in direct causes of mortality (for example, through vehicle collisions or predation by cats or dogs);
- habitat loss, or a decline in the suitability of habitat through land use change;
- habitat fragmentation or severance effects;
- disturbance (noise, visual or direct physical

disturbance such as chasing by dogs) which can lead to a reduction in fitness or abandonment of habitat.

These potential impacts, and appropriate mitigation measures are discussed further below.

In assessing the effects of projects on hares a number of factors need to be taken into account. Firstly, an assessment of the relevant Zone of Influence should be made. As described above, hares have large home ranges and live at relatively low density, dispersing over significant distances. It will therefore rarely be appropriate to consider the population of hares within a small development site in isolation. An understanding of the hare population within the surrounding 1 km$^2$ will probably be needed for understanding impacts at the population level.

The population of hares in the 1 km$^2$ area should be assessed using one or more of the techniques described above and an assessment made of its value on a geographic scale. There is little precedent for this in the literature, and typically in Environmental Statements, populations of hares are assessed as being of Local importance. While this is likely to be an accurate assessment in many cases, there is also a risk that this assessment is based on survey work that identified only a small number of hares, leading to an assumption that there is only a small (and therefore not significant) population, without fully appreciating the ecology of these species. In some cases, (for example large shooting estates with several thousand hares), the population could represent 1 % or more of the national hare population, and here an assessment of 'Regional' value would be more appropriate.

It is also appropriate to take into account the location of the population with respect to the distribution of the species in assessing its value. The same relatively small population of brown hares might be considered of District importance in Cambridgeshire, Local importance in Gloucestershire, and Regional importance in Devon because of their relative status in these counties.

The nature of the effects which might occur as a result of the proposed project should then be assessed. The above list is not exhaustive and will vary with the proposals. Where effects are uncertain, the precautionary principle should be applied.

An assessment should then be made using professional judgement as to whether the potential impacts would be likely to be significant, that is, whether they would affect the conservation status of the hare population. Effects on conservation status might include factors that would cause a permanent reduction in population size or might prevent a depressed population from recovering. This would then be expressed as a significant impact at the (for example) Local level.

## Mortality of animals

Normal causes of mortality in hares include predation by foxes, goshawks, golden eagles, and humans with dogs, guns or snares. Leverets are additionally vulnerable to smaller predators, such as buzzards and kites; there is some evidence that they suffer high mortality from hypothermia in cool, wet conditions. While leverets may be at risk of mortality from site clearance operations, normal precautions to protect ground-nesting birds during their breeding season would also mitigate this impact. In areas where illegal coursing takes place, landowners often cull hares to reduce population density and deter this activity. Road traffic related mortality (*Fig. 4.7*) is considered to be a potentially serious additional source of adult mortality, though there are few studies that document this. Hares reproduce well, with their long breeding season, and their biology is adapted to cope with heavy mortality of the young stages. Conversely, the survival of breeding adults in the face of predation is relatively high. Evidence suggests that the breeding adults in particular are very vulnerable to road mortality. It is possible that roadside verges offer attractive feeding opportunities, or mating activity, especially early in the year at the start of the breeding season, making hares more prone to cross roads. Road traffic mortality can be reduced by sensitive design of the horizontal and vertical alignment of the road. Long straight stretches of road, with wide verges, provide better visibility of oncoming headlights and hence make it less likely that animals will wander onto the carriageway in the path of oncoming vehicles at night.

Advice in relation to the design and positioning of safe crossings for mammals and associated fencing is provided in the Highways Agency's *Design Manual for Roads and Bridges* (Highways Agency 2001), although specific designs/advice in relation to hares is/are not provided. It is not known whether hares will use tunnels or culverts under roads, such as those installed for badgers, but it is likely that they would use 'green bridges' of the type used in mainland Europe. Wide bridges and viaducts, carrying roads high over valleys, would allow hares to pass beneath the road. Putting roads through 'cut and cover' tunnels, rather than cuttings, would retain the integrity of habitat either side of the road. Roadside fencing, perhaps needed to deter deer and other larger mammals, could also deflect hares.

## Habitat loss or loss of key features

Because hares feed on a wide range of grasses, herbs and dwarf shrubs, any conversion of habitat to human infrastructure will equate to some loss of habitat. However, because of their large home ranges and dispersal distances, only very large schemes are likely to have a significant impact at

Brown Hare and Mountain Hare

Brown Hare and Mountain Hare     UK BAP MAMMALS: Interim Guidance for Survey Methodologies, Impact Assessment and Mitigation

*Figure 4.7.* Road traffic related mortality.
Left: A93 Braemar – Blair Atholl road at Glen Shee, Scotland; this road bisects an area of high mountain hare density and hare road casualties are a common sight.  Right: hare road mortality on the A57, Peak District.
[Phil Wheeler; Derek Yalden].

the population level.  Diversification of the restored or surrounding landscape is likely to have potential benefits, and hares' rapid response to deliberate habitat manipulation suggests that it is relatively easy to offer compensation for potential losses. Flower-rich verges, headlands and beetle banks all offer advantages to hares.  Typically a development will result in the loss of habitat quantity and the mitigation strategy will involve replacing this with a smaller quantity of 'better' habitat.  Research on farmland indicates that this sort of 'quality for quantity' habitat replacement can be very effective.

### Habitat fragmentation

Fragmentation of habitats is a typical impact of transport and other linear infrastructure.  Because hares need to circulate between different parts of their habitat as the seasons progress, maintaining habitat integrity is important, and if significant lengths of habitat are fragmented, this could have impacts at the population level.  The measures outlined above to deal with road traffic mortality are equally applicable to deal with fragmentation issues; mitigation should seek to recreate links between patches of isolated habitat.

### Disturbance

Hares live in the open (rather than retreat to a burrow during daylight), making them vulnerable to disturbance from people and especially their dogs. Only the fastest (greyhounds, lurchers, Afghan hounds and salukis) are capable of catching adult hares, but all dogs disturb them, and leverets are much more vulnerable than adults.  This disturbance leads to increased vigilance, which can in turn result in less time spent feeding, and hence poorer

survivorship or breeding success.  Though hares can share human habitats, especially large parks and golf courses, they are generally absent in areas with significant human activity.  Airfields, much of which are human-free grasslands, can be very suitable.

Mitigation for disturbance impacts will normally involve the establishment of some sort of buffer (a physical distance, structures such as walls or fences or structural landscape planting) between hare habitat and the most disturbing activities.  Where this is not possible, it may be appropriate to manage the human activities through a management plan enforced by planning conditions.

### Monitoring

All mitigation measures should be subject to an appropriate scheme of monitoring to ensure that they have been successful.  The nature and extent of this monitoring will depend upon the mitigation implemented.

## 4.8.  Research Requirements

There is very little published information with regard to the effects of projects on hares and the success of mitigation measures.  The following areas are identified as requiring further research:

- what is the relationship between habitat quantity and quality in terms of hare home range size?

- what is the impact of wind turbines on hares (in terms of noise, visual disturbance or electro-magnetic fields)?

- do hares use tunnels under roads?

- is DNA typing of pellets for identification purposes worth considering for distinguishing brown from mountain hares?

UK BAP MAMMALS: Interim Guidance for Survey Methodologies, Impact Assessment and Mitigation    Brown Hare and Mountain Hare

Brown Hare and Mountain Hare

- does mowing severely reduce leveret survival and therefore recruitment?
- what is the impact of road mortality (density of roads, density of traffic, season) on adult hare populations?

## 4.9. References and Bibliography

Batcheler, C. L. (1975) Development of a distance method for deer census from pellet groups. *Journal of Wildlife Management* **39**: 641 – 652.

Harris, S , Morris, P. A., Wray, S. & Yalden, D. W. (1995) *A review of British mammals: population estimates and conservation status of British mammals other than cetaceans*. Joint Nature Conservation Committee, Peterborough.

Harris, S. & Yalden, D. W. (eds) (2008) *Mammals of the British Isles: Handbook,* 4th edition. The Mammal Society.

Highways Agency (2001) *Design Manual for Roads and Bridges (DMRB). Vol. 10. Environmental Design and Management. Section 4. Nature Conservation.* Part 4 HA81/99 (http://www.dft.gov. uk/ha/standards/dmrb/vol10/section4.htm) and Section 5. *Design for Environmental Barriers* HA 65/94 (http://www.dft.gov.uk/ha/standards/dmrb/vol10/section5.htm).

Hutchings, M. R. & Harris, S. (1996) *The current status of the brown hare* (Lepus europaeus) *in Britain*. Joint Nature Conservation Committee, Peterborough.

Kinrade, V., Ewald, J., Smith, A., Newey, S., Iason, G., Thirgood, S. & Raynor, R. (2008) *The distribution of Mountain Hare* (Lepus timidus) *in Scotland* (2006/07). Scottish Natural Heritage Commissioned Report No.278 (ROAME No. R07AC308).

Langbein, J., Hutchings, M. R., Harris, S., Stoate, C., Tapper, S. C. & Wray, S. (1999) Techniques for assessing the numbers of brown hares *Lepus europaeus*. *Mammal Review* **29**: 93–116.

Mallon, D. P. (2001) *The Mountain Hare in the Peak District*. Derbyshire Wildlife Trust, Belper.

Mallon, D., Wheeler, P., Whiteley, D. & Yalden, D. W. (2003) Mountain hares in the Peak District. *British Wildlife* **15**: 110–116.

Mitchell, B., Staines, B. W. & Welch, D. (1977) *The ecology of red deer: a research review relevant to their management in Scotland*. Institute of Terrestrial Ecology, Cambridge.

Neff, D. J. (1968) The pellet group technique for big game trend, census and distribution: a review. *Journal of Wildlife Management* **32**: 597–614.

Newey, S., Bell, M., Enthoven, S. & Thirgood, S. (2003) Can distance sampling and dung plots be used to assess the density of mountain hares *Lepus timidus*? *Wildlife Biology* **9**: 185–192.

Newey, S., Iason, G. & Raynor, R. (2008) The conservation status and management of mountain hares. *Scottish Natural Heritage Commissioned Report* **No. 287** (ROAME No. F05AC316). (http://www.snh.gov.uk/publications-data-and-research/publications/search-the-catalogue/?q=moutain+hare&cat=REP%2CCR).

Newey, S., Potts, J., Baines, D., Castillo, U., Duncan, M., Harrison, A., Ramsay, S., Thirgood, S. & Iason, G. (2011) Development of a reliable method for estimating mountain hare numbers. *Scottish Natural Heritage Commissioned Report* **No. 444**. (http://www.snh.gov.uk/publications-data-and-research/publications/search-the-catalogue/?q=moutain+hare&cat=REP%2CCR).

Petrovan, S. O., Ward, A. I. & Wheeler, P. (2011) Detectability counts when assessing populations for biodiversity targets. *PLoS ONE* **6**: e242 06. doi:10.1371/journal.pone.0024206.

Putman, R. J. (1984) Facts from faeces. *Mammal Review* **14**: 79–97.

Putman, R. J. (1990) Patterns in habitat use – and examination of the available methods. In: *Methods for the Study ofLarge Mammals in Forest Habitats*. (eds Groot Bruinderink, G. T. A. & van Wieren, S. E.) p. 22–31. Research Institute for Nature Management, Netherlands.

Reid, N., Dingerkus, K., Montgomery, W. I., Marnell, F., Jeffrey, R., Lynn, D., Kingston, N. & McDonald, R. A. (2007) Status of hares in Ireland. *Irish Wildlife Manuals* **30**. National Parks and Wildlife Service, Department of Environment, Heritage and Local Government, Dublin, Ireland.

Staines, B. W. & Ratcliffe, P. R. (1987) Estimating the abundance of red deer and roe deer and their current status in Great Britain. *Symposia of the Zoological Society of London* **58**: 131–152

Tapper, S. (1992) *Game heritage: an ecological review from shooting and gamekeeping records*. Game Conservancy, Fordingbridge.

Tapper, S. & Yalden, D. (2010) *The Brown Hare*. The Mammal Society.

Taylor, R. H. & Williams, R. M. (1956) The use of pellet counts for estimating the density of populations of the wild rabbit. *New Zealand Journal of Science and Technology* **38B**: 236–256.

Wigley, T. B. & Johnson, M. K. (1981) Disappearance rates for deer pellets in the southeast. *Journal of Wildlife Management* **45**: 351–253.

# European
# Hedgehog

***Figure 5.1.*** Hedgehog.
[Pat Morris].

# 5. European Hedgehog
*By Pat Morris*

## 5.1. Background Biology

The hedgehog (*Fig. 5.1*) is Britain's only spiny mammal, and is a distant relative of moles and shrews. It is a familiar inhabitant of urban areas, where many householders put out food to attract hedgehogs to their garden. Normally hedgehogs eat macro-invertebrates, especially beetles, worms and caterpillars, but also almost anything edible found at ground level including soft fruit and carrion. They also eat the eggs and chicks of ground-nesting birds, for which they have been treated as vermin by gamekeepers for centuries. Hedgehogs are true hibernators and become less active as the autumn progresses. Large animals may hibernate as early as September if the nights are cold, young and small individuals can remain active until December (especially if given supplementary food). Arousal from hibernation occurs around mid-April, later in the north, but some activity in winter is normal and most hedgehogs will change their hibernation site at least once during the winter months.

Hedgehogs are nocturnal; animals seen out in daylight are generally sick or underweight juveniles struggling to survive. Hedgehogs are generally solitary, but may congregate at attractive feeding areas. Even there they do not behave as social animals, and are often aggressive towards each other. They are not territorial, but normally avoid other hedgehogs. Males are more active than females (at least in the main breeding season), may travel 3 km or more in a night, seeking females and food, and may use 50 ha or more in the course of a summer season. Females normally travel about 1 km in a night, with a home range of about 10 ha in a season. Home ranges of both sexes appear to be smaller in forest and garden habitats, although there is evidence suggesting that some individuals may be nomadic and wander widely. Male ranges normally overlap with those of several females; males change their daytime nest frequently (rarely using the same one for more than a few days) whereas females, even when not breeding, tend to return to the same nest for many consecutive days. Adult hedgehogs do not share nests simultaneously, although males may visit nests previously used by females. Population densities average about one hedgehog per hectare in good habitat, with temporary clustering in favoured nesting and feeding sites.

Male and female hedgehogs are promiscuous; there is no pair bond. Mating occurs from about May onwards; litters are mostly born in June–July. Females may have a second litter if the first is lost or reared early. Late litters are born in September, sometimes to young females too small to breed earlier in the year, and many of these offspring will be too small to survive the winter. Normal litter size is four to five; six or more is unusual. About 20 % of young die before weaning, especially in larger litters. Females probably rarely raise more than three offspring to independence. Juveniles may start to leave the nest after three weeks, are weaned after four to six weeks, and become fully independent (dispersing and living solitary lives) at six weeks. At this stage they weigh about 120–150 g and are very vulnerable. Many are taken into captivity by animal carers and released later. Juveniles that fail to attain a weight of 450 g by the beginning of hibernation (normally about October) are unlikely to survive the winter. Those juveniles that do hibernate successfully breed at an age of one year and in subsequent years until old age. Annual adult mortality is 20–30 % and about four animals in a thousand reach seven years old.

Threats to hedgehogs include pesticides. These (particularly slug pellets) may affect hedgehogs directly but also reduce food availability. Badgers are an increasingly significant danger as they prey upon hedgehogs, but also compete with them for food. Every badger eats about the same amount as five hedgehogs, so increasing badger populations (now happening nationwide) exert significant pressure on hedgehog numbers and may have already resulted in local population losses. Where badgers exceed about 15 km$^{-2}$, hedgehog extinction is likely. Foxes have also been reported to be a significant predation threat in urban areas. Population fragmentation is likely to be another threat, particularly in urban areas with impenetrable fencing. Wide roads and expansive arable fields are likely to restrict hedgehog movements in rural areas. Rivers are less of a problem as hedgehogs can and do swim across them although they often drown in garden ponds as a result of being unable to climb out. Roadkill in Britain is probably about 15,000 hedgehogs per year, but it is unclear how significant this is in population terms. Significant numbers are also killed by other anthropogenic causes, such as mowing machines and garden strimmers (wildlife hospitals receive many hedgehogs injured in this way); dogs and cats. Hedgehogs will readily nest in garden bonfire heaps and many are injured or incinerated as a result. Disease and parasites (especially lungworm) also account for some deaths, but failure to hibernate successfully is a major cause of mortality among juveniles.

*Figure 5.2.* **Good garden habitat for hedgehogs.**
A lawn, plenty of shrubbery, compost heaps and a bowl of suitable food offer good habitat for hedgehogs. Ten or more animals may come to use the same garden as part of their home range, although few may actually nest there.
[Pat Morris].

*Figure 5.3.* **Hedgehog winter nest.**
Typical habitat for a winter nest site (left) and a winter nest, broken open (right).
[Pat Morris].

## 5.2. Habitat Requirements

Hedgehogs occur in a wide variety of habitat types including, for example, grasslands, forests and suburban areas (*Fig. 5.2*). They do little harm (except to ground-nesting birds) and are voracious consumers of garden pests. They appear to be limited by availability of food and nesting sites; with the latter perhaps being more critical.

### Hibernacula

Hedgehogs need a secure site for winter nesting and suitable materials with which to build the nest (*Fig. 5.3*). For up to six months this is their only protection from the worst weather of the year. Winter nests (*Fig. 5.3*) are made using the naturally fallen leaves from deciduous trees. Large leaves (e.g. horse chestnut) are unsuitable as are small ones (e.g. birch). Oak and similar leaves are ideal, and are made into a laminated heap that surrounds the hibernating animal with at least 5 cm of tightly packed leaves. These nests are weatherproof and resist decay for up to 18 months. Pinnate leaves (ferns) or grass strands are less suitable nesting material as they cannot be packed flat and tight enough to resist percolation by rain. Nests are normally built underneath some structure that lends support from above, for example, a garden shed, pile of brushwood or sprawling brambles. The winter nest is a crucial factor in hedgehog distribution and habitat use, leading to absence from certain habitats, areas above the tree line and (in northern Europe) beyond the limits of deciduous trees. The specific need for suitable leaves and physical support is probably why hedgehogs are rare or absent in conifer woodland, marshy areas, heathland and moorland. Similarly, lack of supportive vegetation (due to 'tidying up') limits where the animals can live in gardens and urban parks, as well as in open habitats such as arable fields. Some individuals may hibernate underground in rabbit burrows, tree stumps or natural cavities where these are available.

### Summer nests

Summer nesting requirements are less critical. Females need to build a similar nest of leaves, scrap paper etc. in which to raise their young. Otherwise hedgehogs (especially males) simply shelter in a suitable place at the end of the night, often returning to use the same place on consecutive days. These shelters (*Fig. 5.4*) are frequently located in long grass or other rank vegetation (e.g. at field margins or road verges) where they are highly vulnerable to mowing machines. Non-fatal disturbance to nesting hedgehogs does not result in their running away, although disturbance to females and young nestlings usually results in the latter being eaten or abandoned by their mother. Older nestlings will be carried or led away to another nest to complete their development.

### Food and feeding

Dry sandy soils tend to offer fewer worms and other large invertebrates, similarly cold upland areas and acid soils. Conversely, moist rich soils offer ideal feeding areas especially where grass is grazed short, making access easier. Cattle or horse grazing also adds manure, attracting large numbers of additional potential prey. Dry weather limits the availability of worms especially, and may seriously affect females attempting to raise young.

Ideal habitats thus have good feeding opportunities juxtaposed with suitable nesting areas and sources of nesting material. Pastureland with small fields separated by hedges and copses is good hedgehog habitat. Amenity grasslands, including the rough areas of golf courses, are also suitable provided that nesting opportunities exist nearby and pesticide use is restrained. Urban garden habitats (including cemeteries and allotments) are also suitable, especially where nesting is possible and supplementary food is put out for pets and wildlife.

## 5.3. Status and Distribution

The hedgehog is found throughout the UK (apart from the habitats mentioned above), including Ireland, the Isle of Man and various smaller islands (*Fig. 5.5*). Most (perhaps all) of the latter have been colonised as a result of deliberate or accidental translocation by humans. On some smaller islands where ground-nesting birds were previously secure from other predators, hedgehogs may become a threat to bird numbers. Within Britain, hedgehogs are one of the mammals that appear to thrive in urban areas and their surroundings. However, increased density of building, habitat barriers and other factors are probably causing piecemeal extinction and gradual exclusion from many such areas used in the past.

There is abundant and consistent evidence from gamekeeper records, structured roadkill surveys and anecdote that hedgehogs are becoming scarcer. During the ten years prior to 2000, hedgehog numbers appear to have declined by at least 30 %, and numbers had probably been falling steadily for many years before that. However, hedgehogs remain abundant on some islands and also in localised patches of highly suitable habitat, notably suburban gardens, where a dozen or more individuals may visit the same place within a few weeks.

## 5.4. Legislative Protection

The hedgehog is listed on Schedule 6 of the Wildlife and Countryside Act, 1981, which prohibits the taking or killing of these animals by certain

*Figure 5.4.* **Typical hedgehog temporary nest.**
During warm summer weather the animals may simply lie up in long grass or dense vegetation without building a proper nest.
[Pat Morris].

Hedgehog

*Figure 5.5.* **The distribution map of hedgehogs for the British Isles.**

Black indicates regular or usual range; dark grey, scattered but regular occurrence; light grey, rare occurrences, vagrants, or scarce and beyond the regular range.

[from: Harris & Yalden (2008) *Mammals of the British Isles: Handbook,* 4th edition. Mammal Society; with minor amendments].

methods. The only relevant act covered is that of trapping, but hedgehogs continue to be caught or killed by gamekeepers as an incidental result of trapping 'vermin' to protect gamebirds. 'Mercy killing' and capture for the purpose of nursing sick and injured animals is allowed for. The Wild Mammals (Protection) Act of 1996, essentially animal welfare legislation, made it an offence to kick, mutilate, burn or otherwise cause deliberate cruelty to wild mammals. The hedgehog was a particular beneficiary being a frequent victim of such abuse. However, this will have negligible effect at the population level and there is no protection for their habitats.

## 5.5. Summary of UK BAP Status and Recommended Actions

The hedgehog was added to the list of UK BAP species in 2007, and is on the Biodiversity Lists for England and Wales (listed as a Species of Principal Importance under the NERC Act 2006), and Northern Ireland (listed as a Priority Species in the Northern Ireland Priority Species List, March 2010).

The BAP recommended actions for the hedgehog are (http://www.jncc.gov.uk/_speciespages/2253.pdf):

- carry out national surveys to determine where hedgehogs still occur, especially in expanding urban areas; repeat and expand monitoring studies regularly to confirm suspected decline and determine if decline is varying in different geographical areas;

- carry out studies of habitat use and differential population densities to see which habitats are most and least suitable to sustain hedgehog populations to ensure conservation efforts are focused in the best areas;

- encourage (a) conservation of hedgerow systems and wooded areas near arable fields etc.; (b) extensive (i.e. non-intensive) farming practices; (c) smaller field sizes; (d) greater field margins; and (e) stop and reverse fragmentation of farmland; raise awareness of and urge people to consider the need for providing hibernacula in otherwise 'tidy' garden habitats and encourage better management of urban sites;

- investigate the effect on populations of incidental take by gamekeepers (several thousand per year); if necessary, improve legal protection; clarify and publicise legal obligations facing trappers likely to kill or injure hedgehogs in traps set for other species;

- carry out a study of population genetics to discover to what extent population fragmentation is occurring, with a sub-section of the project (marking, radio tracking)

determining the extent to which roads act as dispersal barriers.

## 5.6. Survey Methodology

Surveys normally aim at establishing either presence or abundance although arguably there may not be a need to establish an exact population size for EcIA purposes. Neither are likely to be successful between October and May (when most hedgehogs are hibernating). Although a search for winter nests may reveal a few in certain habitats, this will be a time-consuming activity that is unlikely to find all of the animals present except perhaps in a very small area that is subjected to a fingertip search. Hedgehogs are most numerous and most active in September, especially during periods of warm, moist weather at night.

### Presence

Asking local people if they have seen hedgehogs, dead or alive, is often the best way of establishing presence (although it cannot be used as evidence of absence). Misidentification is unlikely and many people take notice when they see road casualties or the animals visit their garden. Roadkills are a useful indication of presence, often the only one. Flattened, sun dried carcasses are very resilient and can remain identifiable for at least four weeks, making them prominent over a longer time than many species, especially rabbits that are more likely to be removed by scavengers.

Trapping for hedgehogs requires a licence issued under the (Wildlife and Countryside Act 1981 (as amended)) from the relevant licensing authority (see Section 1.6) and needs to allow for twice-daily checking of traps (dawn and dusk). Cage traps need to be set under cover along linear features such as hedges and walls. They are likely to be most effective at gaps where animals pass through. Dog food or rabbit viscera make the best bait. However, trapping success is low and incidental capture of rats and birds is highly likely, as is disturbance by inquisitive dogs and cattle. Under normal circumstances trapping is unlikely to be a cost-effective way of demonstrating presence. Tracking tunnels (where animals leave footprints (*Fig. 5.6*) on a specially-inked tray) have been shown to detect hedgehogs; more information on this methodology is available from The Mammal Society (http://88.208.205.92/index.php?option=com_content&view=article&id=373&Itemid=359). Research in 2011–12, sponsored by the People's Trust for Endangered Species and the British Hedgehog Preservation Society, aims to establish how many such tunnels are needed and for how long, in order to assess likely presence/absence. Preliminary findings indicate that tunnels are more effective at detecting hedgehog presence

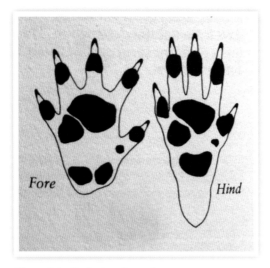

**Figure 5.6.** Hedgehog footprints.
Hedgehogs have fleshy feet and prominent claws.
Size varies a lot with age.
[Pat Morris].

**Figure 5.7.** Hedgehog faeces.
These are about finger-sized and usually have beetle elytra prominently visible
on the surface.
[Pat Morris].

**Figure 5.8.** Artificial nest boxes for hedgehogs.
A German model of a winter nest box (left) and a cheap Correx plastic shelter (right), which can be pushed into a hedge or under a shed to
provide a cavity in which a hedgehog may build a nest.
[Pat Morris].

than spotlight surveys, and take considerably less effort to use (R. Yarnell, *pers. comm.*). Another possible detection method, based on the presence of host-specific parasites in faecal samples, was also being tested in 2011–12.

Searching for hedgehogs at night is a useful means of confirming presence and also the main method for attempting estimates of abundance. A powerful lamp is needed, scanning the ground to either side as the observer walks along. Occasional pauses to listen for rustling are useful as hedgehogs are generally careless about keeping quiet, apparently confident of their spiny protection. Searches are best done in short grass habitats or along linear

features such as woodland rides or rural lanes. Cold or wet nights are less productive than warm ones. A line of searchers 10 m apart may be used to comb large areas; single observers normally walk a straight line transect. This offers the prospect of using distance sampling methodology to estimate abundance (numbers per hectare). However, the normal encounter rates (less than one per hour of searching unless whole families are found) mean that transects have to be replicated and need to be 1 km or longer in similar habitat type. For practical reasons, these requirements are rarely met, and as a result the counts do not generate consistent or statistically reliable results. Estimating actual abundance is rarely needed and unlikely to provide reliable data for comparison with other sites. Some dogs are good at finding hedgehogs and their help may be enlisted to considerable benefit. However, this may fall foul of anti-hunting legislation, which makes using dogs to trail mammals illegal, although that possibility has not yet been tested in court. Similarly, the use of 'dazzling lights' to seek Schedule 6 species (like the hedgehog) at night is technically illegal unless a licence is carried. This too has not been tested in court.

Less useful survey methods include searching for faeces. These are distinctive (about 1 cm diameter, irregular shape, about 3 cm long) (*Fig. 5.7*). They are usually black, crinkly in appearance and stuffed with fragments of beetle elytra, which form black shiny additions to the surface. Cat and dog droppings lack these and fox droppings are usually larger, grey and mostly formed of fur and fragments of bone. Fur and bone are not normally present in hedgehog droppings and never form their main component. Hedgehog droppings are normally found singly, not in latrines or clusters, and are easiest to see in short grass such as garden lawns. Searching for footprints is likely to be a waste of time unless areas of fine-grained soft mud are available. Even here, there may be difficulty in reliably separating footprints of hedgehogs from those of squirrels, polecats or mink. Although hedgehogs may use the same paths regularly, trails are unlikely to be a reliable indication of presence without some other form of confirmation.

Roadkill counts have been shown to reflect actual population density in rabbits and there is reason to believe that roadkills provide a useful index of abundance in hedgehogs and other species. At present there is no way of relating numbers of hedgehogs killed to numbers alive, but hedgehog roadkills are not simply a reflection of traffic density (Morris 2010).

### Identifying important features

Nesting sites and materials are vital features of hedgehog habitat. Absence of deciduous trees or absence of sheltering supportive structures (bushes, log piles or other places where nests could be made underneath) will suggest an absence of hedgehogs. Availability of such features is not evidence of hedgehog presence, but it is an essential requirement for them. Similarly, availability of macro-invertebrates (or artificial sources such as pet food bowls) is necessary for hedgehog survival. Their presence is not evidence that hedgehogs live nearby, but their absence is a negative factor and their continued availability is something that needs to be identified and protected. Searching for nests is unlikely to be productive unless a dog is used (see above), but even dogs may be unable to locate hibernacula by smell.

## 5.7. Impact Assessment, Mitigation, Compensation and Enhancement

It is not straightforward to assess the impacts of a project on hedgehogs. Despite the decline in its population, it is a widespread species relatively common in some areas, and significant adverse effects are unlikely unless the scale of the project is particularly large. That said, however, certain types of impact can disproportionately affect hedgehogs over a large area due to their home range size and particular habitat requirements. These are likely to result in significant impacts at a Local level, and examples are described below.

### Habitat loss

Habitat loss could be significant if it affects a prime feeding area. For example, hedgehogs will travel over 500 m to feed at desirable sites (such as a food bowl in a favoured garden). Thus draining a small area of moist grassland rich in hedgehog food or sealing it with concrete may affect the hedgehog population over an area of 75 ha or more. Similarly, a dozen or more hedgehogs may use a strip of hedgerow or patch of sprawling bramble only 200 m long as the site for their winter nests. Removal of such features will be highly damaging as hedgehogs from a wide area may be forced to congregate in such patches due to lack of other suitable winter nesting sites nearby.

For some species, loss of nesting sites can be mitigated by providing nest boxes. Various designs are available for the hedgehog (*Fig. 5.8*), but most are expensive and unnecessarily elaborate. Nevertheless, hedgehog nest boxes are used by them and cannot do any harm. They are unlikely to do a lot of good. Provision and maintenance of natural nesting sites and materials is likely to be more cost-effective.

Mitigation should include a requirement for ongoing management to commit to not removing potential nesting or feeding sites (to 'tidy up' for example). Planted screening vegetation such as tree lines could usefully be supplemented with bramble or other low-growing shrubs that provide shelter and nesting sites (also some food from invertebrates using the moist environment underneath). Log piles and brushwood heaps should be encouraged, not cleared away. Potential feeding areas should be mown or grazed to maintain short grass habitat. Residents should be encouraged to put out moist food for hedgehogs, although this cannot be a complete substitute for natural foods. For further information, see Morris (2010).

### Habitat fragmentation

Very large open areas such as arable fields, motorways or airports are likely to be unattractive to hedgehogs and unfavourable habitat. They constitute a form of semi-permeable barrier, forcing

*Figure 5.9.*  **Potential barriers that may lead to habitat fragmentation.**
Left: larch-lap fence with a concrete strip along the ground.  Right: new concrete safety barriers separating carriageways on a motorway.
[Pat Morris].

*Figure 5.10.*  **Pond and cattle grid escape ramps.**
A small ramp (left) will help hedgehogs to escape from smooth-sided ponds in which they will otherwise drown and, (right) from cattle grids.
Over 50 hedgehogs have been found dead in a single cattle grid.
[Pat Morris].

*Figure 5.11.*  **Roads (left) and heavy machinery (right) are potential sources of mortality.**
About 15,000 hedgehogs are killed on Britain's roads each year.  In warm weather hedgehogs lie up in dense grass and shrubs, the very places
that are subjected to rough mowing to control vegetation height; how many animals are killed as a result is not known.
[Pat Morris].

the animals to live and feed around the periphery. The population then begins to consist of linear segments, vulnerable to further fragmentation. Ensuring the continuity and suitability of peripheral linear habitats then becomes an important mitigation factor. Habitat fragmentation also results from the construction of walls and impermeable fencing (e.g. larch-lap with a concrete strip along the ground, *Fig. 5.9*). Such barriers cannot be climbed and are often difficult to burrow under. Their use is becoming increasingly frequent in urban infill developments, fragmenting populations of hedgehogs (and those of amphibians and reptiles too). Small gaps under such a fence or wall might benefit hedgehogs particularly in new housing developments that have all the (small) gardens isolated behind impermeable fences. There is scientific evidence that roads inhibit free movement by hedgehogs. The recent policy of constructing a metre-high wall between carriageways on motorways and trunk roads (*Fig. 5.9*) creates total barriers extending for many kilometres. Thus roads should be considered as increasingly important factors in fragmenting populations, probably isolating small groups of animals that are not viable in the long term.

There is evidence that hedgehogs (and small mammals) are deterred by the presence of roads (Rondinini & Doncaster 2002), even narrow ones (MacPherson *et al*. 2011), although they will use road verges. There has been no research done to study specifically hedgehogs and motorways. There is no specific advice from the Highways Agency relating to hedgehogs and habitat fragmentation. There is no a priori reason why hedgehogs should not use mitigation, in the form of overbridges, underpasses, and culverts (such as badger tunnels), designed for other species. A study in Spain (Yanes *et al*. 1995) showed that hedgehogs used culverts under roads and railways.

### Direct mortality

Housing and amenity developments often include artificial ponds or outdoor swimming pools. These are a frequent danger to hedgehogs, which can swim but cannot climb out of smooth-sided pools (or cattle grids). A small section of wire mesh, a ramp or pile of bricks should be provided wherever possible to allow the animals to climb out and escape (*Fig. 5.10*). A gently shelving edge (for ponds anyway) is desirable for this and many other reasons.

Roads may be identified as a notable cause of potential mortality (*Fig. 5.11*) and may perhaps even eliminate a local population. Although evidence to support this may be hard to provide, one study in the Netherlands (Huiser & Bergers 2000) suggested that roads and traffic were likely to reduce hedgehog density by about 30 %.

However, a more recent study in urban areas in the UK (Dowding *et al*. 2010) found that hedgehogs were significantly more active after midnight, when there was a marked reduction in vehicle traffic, potentially reducing the risks associated with human activities, although not eliminating the risk as they did not avoid crossing roads per se. Fencing specifically to discourage hedgehogs from crossing roads is possible (using smooth metal, 50 cm high for example), but hardly practical and anyway adds to the population fragmentation threat posed by roads for hedgehogs and many other small species. As discussed above, overbridges and underpasses may be used by hedgehogs.

Use of heavy machinery during daylight hours (*Fig. 5.11*), or burning scrub and long grass, are likely to kill or injure nesting hedgehogs as this species reacts to disturbance by rolling up and remaining stationary rather than running away. Hibernating animals cannot take evasive action as they need at least 15–20 minutes to arouse sufficiently to become mobile. Accidental killing can only be avoided by a very detailed search of the site for nesting hedgehogs, some of which may be under brushwood heaps or down rabbit burrows for example. Any hedgehogs found can simply be taken away and released at night in suitable habitats (preferably where other hedgehogs are present). Hedgehogs are very phlegmatic animals and can cope with casual translocation like this, although they may attempt to 'home' unless removed to a distant site. Hibernating animals can also be woken up and released, provided the weather is mild. Arousal in winter and building new nests is natural behaviour. Release in frosty conditions and snow should be avoided. Rescued animals can be taken to the RSPCA/SSPCA or a specialist hedgehog care.[6]

### Disturbance

Hedgehogs are not shy animals and disturbance is unlikely to affect them significantly. They can be handled, marked and released, even picked up by dogs, without showing signs of distress. Very occasionally a hedgehog will emit a scream if handled, but countless handlings, disturbance to hedgehogs feeding at food bowls, traffic noise and garden floodlights all appear insufficient to cause them to relocate. Indeed some hedgehogs become so used to being handled or observed by artificial light that they fail to show any reaction at all. Installation of permanent street lighting does not cause desertion of a site, but may result in the animals spending more time under cover

---

[6] List of addresses and contact numbers are available from the British Hedgehog Preservation Society (01584 890801) or see their website http://www.britishhedgehogs.org.uk

and might dissuade some of them from using key feeding areas.

Translocation is frequently suggested as mitigation when large-scale impacts are envisaged; however, translocation is discouraged and should only be attempted as a last resort. As hedgehogs are absent from various Hebridean islands and rare/vagrant over large parts of the Highlands, or are 'beyond the regular range' of the species, translocations should not be made into these areas since the Wildlife and Natural Environment (Scotland) Act 2011 prohibits the release of any wild animal outside of its natural range. Translocated hedgehogs do fare well provided they are released into suitable habitat, preferably similar to that from which they have been removed (Morris 2010). Many hundreds of rehabilitated hedgehogs are released every year after a period in veterinary care. Even juvenile animals with no previous experience of life in the wild can cope well. Receptor sites should have the beneficial habitat features described above and also an existing hedgehog population (if hedgehogs are absent then perhaps the site is unsuitable). Translocated animals integrate well with resident populations (Morris 2010). Soft release methods can do no harm, but there is no evidence that they are necessary, indeed they have been rarely used. Most rehabilitated animals, for example, are hard released. A study of released rehabilitated animals in Devon revealed that few of the animals involved took any notice of supplementary food provided and most ignored it. Although significant new populations have been established from fewer than five animals, attempts to start a new population using translocated animals should not be encouraged, particularly translocation to hedgehog-free islands. Similarly, translocation to walled gardens (deemed 'safe' by their owners) is not a good idea as hedgehogs normally range over much larger areas (half a golf course for example), and constrained space may lead to high population densities with consequent aggression between males.

## 5.8.  Research Requirements

A major research and public awareness campaign is being spearheaded by the People's Trust for Endangered Species and the British Hedgehog Preservation Society, with three main objectives:

- to identify the best way of monitoring population changes;
- to establish how hedgehogs use arable landscapes;
- to test two methods that ecological consultants might use to establish presence (and potential absence) of hedgehogs.

This work began in 2011, along with a public awareness campaign (called 'Hedgehog Stree' – see http://www.ptes.org/index.php?page=396) on behalf of the hedgehog.

Additional requirements include:

- repeating previous hedgehog surveys to indicate whether hedgehog numbers have changed;
- determining how much time is required to reliably find hedgehogs by observation on different sized sites;
- investigating how fragmented on a local scale hedgehog populations are; very few radio-tracking studies have been done to determine use of habitats by hedgehogs; there are likely to be increasing threats to hedgehog populations from increased patchiness in their urban/semi-urban environment (for example, as bigger gardens are cleared and split into sites with lots of smaller gardens); ascertaining how hedgehogs use/do not use overbridges, underpasses and culverts needs addressing;
- investigating if it is possible to develop a Habitat Suitability Index to evaluate the suitability of habitat for hedgehogs, akin to that used for great crested newts.

## 5.9.  References and Bibliography

Dowding, C. V., Harris, S. & Poulton, S. (2010) Nocturnal ranging behaviour of urban hedgehogs, *Erinaceus europaeus*, in relation to risk and reward. *Animal Behaviour* **80**: 13–21.

Hof, A. R. & Bright, P. W. (2009) The value of green-spaces in built-up areas for western hedgehogs. *Lutra* **52**: 69–82.

Hof, A. R. & Bright, P. W. (2010a) The value of agri-environment schemes for macro-invertebrate feeders: hedgehogs on arable farms in Britain. *Animal Conservation* **13**: 467–473.

Hof, A. R. & Bright, P. W. (2010b) The impact of grassy field margins on macro-invertebrate abundance in adjacent arable fields. *Agriculture, Ecosystems & Environment* **139**: 280–283.

Huiser, M. P. & Bergers, P. J. M. (2000) The effect of roads and traffic on hedgehog (*Erinaceus europaeus*) populations. *Biological Conservation* **95**: 111–116.

MacPherson, D., MacPherson, J. L. & Morris, P. (2011) Rural roads as barriers to the movement of small mammals. *Applied Ecology and Environmental Research* **9**: 167–180.

Morris, P. A. (1998) Hedgehog rehabilitation in perspective. *Veterinary Record* **143**: 633–636.

Morris, P. (2010) *The New Hedgehog Book*. Whittet Books, Stansted, Essex.

Morris, P. A. & Reeve, N. J. (2008) Hedgehog (*Erinaceus europaeus*). In: Harris, S. & Yalden, D. W. (eds) *Mammals of the British Isles: Handbook,* 4th edition. pp 241–248.

Rondinini, C. & Doncaster, C. P. (2002) Roads as barriers to movement for hedgehogs. *Functional Ecology* **16**: 504–509.

Warwick, H., Morris, P. and Walker, D. (2006) Survival and weight changes of hedgehogs (*Erinaceus europaeus*) translocated from the Hebrides to Mainland Scotland. *Lutra* **49**: 89–102.

Yanes, M., Velasco, J. M. & Suarez, F. (1995) Permeability of roads and railways to vertebrates: The importance of culverts. *Biological Conservation* **71**: 217–222.

# Wildcat

*Figure 6.1.* Wildcat.
[Neville Buck].

# 6. Wildcat

*By Andrew C. Kitchener*

## 6.1. Background Biology

The wildcat *Felis silvestris* (*Fig. 6.1*) is the only surviving native member of the cat family, the Felidae, in the UK. The information below is taken mainly from Kitchener (1995) and Kitchener & Daniels (2008). Males have a total length, including tail, of 823–981 mm and weigh 3.8–7.3 kg, while females are smaller, reaching 730–895 mm and weighing 2.4–4.7 kg. In external appearance they look similar to striped tabby domestic cats *Felis catus*, but wildcats have fewer distinct flank stripes, are more robust and have relatively longer legs. The tail is bushy with a distinctive black blunt tip. Owing to considerable introgressive hybridisation, there is a high proportion of hybrid cats among the wild-living cat population; in hybrids stripes break down into spots especially on the rump and the tail tends to be more tapering. White paws are also good indicators of hybridisation. Wildcats are exclusively carnivorous, feeding primarily on rabbits and small mammals, including voles and mice. Although they predate birds, research has shown that their impact is negligible compared with that of foxes and other predators.

Wildcats are solitary hunters, mainly crepuscular and nocturnal, but they may be active throughout 24 hours in winter. They maintain a dispersed social system, whereby a male's exclusive home range overlaps with one or more exclusive female home ranges, although if prey is concentrated, the ranges of each sex will show some degree of overlap. Home-range sizes vary depending on abundance of prey, ranging from 8–18 km² in the west of Scotland, where rabbit population densities may be very low, to 0.3–6 km² in the east where rabbits may be very abundant. The main method of communication is scent marking and includes spraying urine against prominent objects such as rocks and trees in a home range, leaving exposed scats, scratching tree bark and cheek rubbing.

Females tend to have one litter per year, usually born in Apri–May after a gestation period of about 65 days, but a second litter may be born as late as August if the first litter is lost. Older and very young females may also breed later in the year. Average litter size is 3–4, but ranges 1–8. Young are usually independent by 5–6 months old.

## 6.2. Habitat Requirements

Wildcats are usually associated with mixed-age woodland habitats but, owing to the low proportion of woodland cover in the UK, they may also frequent more open habitats. Today they are found in the margins of mountain and moorland with rough grazing and mostly with forests and crops (Easterbee *et al.* 1991) (see *Fig. 6.2*). There are regional differences; in the west of Scotland they are mostly found in uplands with rough grazing and moorland with some pastures, whereas in the east wildcats are found in marginal agricultural areas with moorlands, pasturelands and woodlands. Wildcats avoid exposed coasts, low hills dominated by bogs, high mountains with well-drained moorlands, fertile lowlands with intensive agriculture, and industrialised and urbanised areas. They are usually found below 500 m above sea level (a.s.l.), but may venture up to 800 m a.s.l. Poor weather may drive wildcats from more open habitats into woodland and scrub for shelter. Young forestry plantations provide important habitat, because they are protected from grazing and support high population densities of small mammals.

Den sites (*Fig. 6.3*) are usually among large rocks and boulders and rocky cairns on hillsides, or in fox earths, badger setts, rabbit burrows and among tree roots. There is no detailed information about den-site usage in Scotland, although it is expected that, like wildcats in mainland Europe, they will have access to several dens within their home range, although females use different den sites for giving birth to and rearing kittens than those they use for resting or sheltering from bad weather. In France wildcats used (non-breeding) dens mostly from late autumn to early spring and the areas around dens from late spring to late autumn. From October to February, wildcats returned frequently on consecutive days to resting dens at the same location (with one den selected more often), while in spring males changed their resting sites almost daily (Stahl & Leger 1992). In the Harz region of Germany the den sites of three male wildcats were investigated by Jerosch *et al.* (2010). These daytime resting sites were situated either in dense vegetation, including in bushes, unmown meadows or crops such as cereals and oilseed rape or, where undergrowth was sparse, in deadwood, including among upturned tree roots, and among the fallen crowns and trunks of trees, or in brushwood. No den sites were underground, in contrast to Scotland, where woodland cover is very low in comparison with mainland Europe. The microhabitat up to 2 m away was dominated by a herb layer > 50 cm tall. Den sites were typically at forest edges, where small mammal prey are more abundant, but were not apparently affected by human-made structures. Most of the den sites were at ground level, but 14 % were in trees or on hunting hides, where they may offer wildcats sight of rivals, prey and predators, such as eagle

*Figure 6.2.* Good wildcat habitat.
[Kerry Kilshaw].

*Figure 6.3.* Wildcat kitten entering den site.
[Keith Baxby].

owls *Bubo bubo* and dense vegetation may hide them from the latter. Only about half of dens gave protection from the rain. Den sites were spread widely over home ranges, but occupied dens were at least 25 m apart and about half faced south.

## 6.3. Status and Distribution

After centuries of hunting, persecution and habitat loss, wildcats became extinct throughout most of Britain by the early 20th century. They survived mostly in the north-west Highlands, although it is possible that small pockets survived elsewhere in northern Scotland. They are now found only in Scotland north of the central belt between Edinburgh and Glasgow (see *Fig. 6.4*), owing to avoidance of intensive agriculture, and urban and industrialised areas. In the 1990s it was estimated that about 3,500 wildcat survived in Scotland (Harris *et al*. 1995), but a study of road and other casualties suggested that only 12 % were likely to be pure wildcats, the rest being hybrids. This suggests that perhaps only 400 wildcats survived in Scotland then. A survey published in 2010 by Scottish Natural Heritage (SNH) (Davis & Gray 2010) concluded that the general pattern of wildcat distribution had not changed since the last detailed survey in the 1980s. Wildcats were found to be

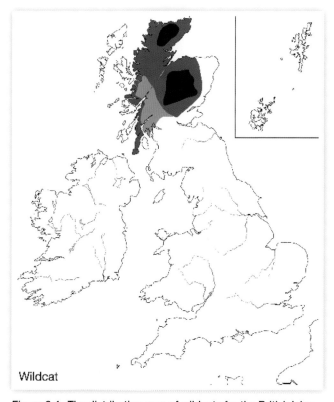

Wildcat

***Figure 6.4.*** **The distribution map of wildcats for the British Isles.**
Black indicates regular or usual range; dark grey, scattered but regular occurrence; light grey, rare occurrences, vagrants, or scarce and beyond the regular range. Note that details of the latest wildcat survey can be found in Davis & Gray (2010).
[from: Harris & Yalden (2008) *Mammals of the British Isles: Handbook,* 4th edition. Mammal Society; with minor amendments].

most abundant in Aberdeenshire, followed by Inverness-shire, Ardnamurchan and Morvern, with lower numbers of reports in Perthshire and the Central Highlands.

## 6.4. Legislative Protection

Wildcats are listed on Annex IV of the European Directive 92/43/EEC on the conservation of natural habitats of wild fauna and flora, which lists species in need of strict protection. This has been transposed into domestic legislation through The Conservation (Natural Habitat, &c.) Regulations, 1994 (amended in Scotland in 2004, 2007 and 2008). It is listed in Schedule 2 of these regulations as a 'European protected species of animal'. Wildcats were first fully protected through inclusion on Schedule 5 of the Wildlife and Countryside Act 1981 (amended in 1988). However, the Conservation (Natural Habitats, &c.) Amendment (Scotland) Regulations 2007 removed the wildcat and other European protected species of animal from Schedule 5 of the Wildlife and Countryside Act 1981, so that its full legal protection is through the 1994 Act and its amendments.

Under this legislation it is illegal to: deliberately, or recklessly capture, injure, kill or harass wildcats; disturb them in a den or other structure used for shelter or protection; disturb them while rearing or caring for their young; obstruct or deny access to breeding and resting sites; cause disturbance that will affect local distribution or abundance of wildcats, or impair their ability to survive, reproduce and rear young; and damage or destroy breeding or resting sites. It is also illegal to keep, transport, sell, exchange or offer for sale or exchange any wildcat or any part or derivative of one, if obtained after 10th June 1994.

## 6.5. Summary of UK BAP Status and Recommended Actions

Wildcats featured on the revised UK BAP list of Priority Species and Habitats in 2007, the Scottish Biodiversity List (under the Nature Conservation (Scotland) Act 2004) and were listed on SNH's Five Year Species Action Plan as a species for conservation action (SNH 2007).

The BAP recommended actions for the wildcat are (http://www.jncc.gov.uk/_speciespages/2272.pdf):

- determine the distribution and status of the Scottish wildcat;

- evaluate risks from genetic introgression through investigation of feral/domestic cat distribution and develop policies to minimise these;

- identify priority wildcat habitats or sites and prepare best practice guidance for management.

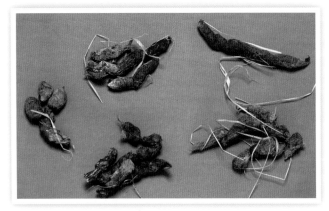

*Figure 6.5.* **Wildcat field signs.**
Top left: footprint. Bottom left: scats. Right: tracks in the snow.
[Will Boyd-Wallis; National Museums Scotland; Will Boyd-Wallis].

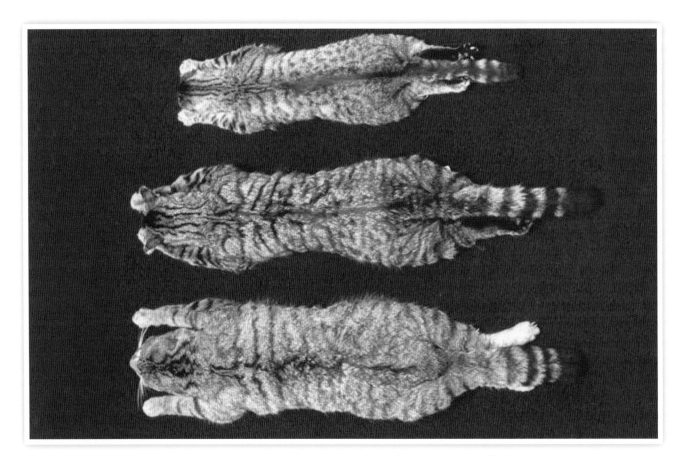

*Figure 6.6.* **Dorsal views of pelages of Scottish wildcat (bottom), hybrid (centre) and domestic cat (top).**
[National Museums Scotland].

## 6.6. Survey Methodology

The survey methodology is based largely on Forestry Commission Scotland Guidance Note 35d: *Forest operations and wildcats in Scotland* (FCS 2009) and the methodology developed by Adrian Davis (*pers. comm.*). Before surveying, it would be advisable to check for historic records of wildcats from such sources as the National Biodiversity Network interactive map,[7] local Biological Records Centres[8] and SNH.[9] As a general guide, wildcats may be expected to occur anywhere north of the central belt (between Edinburgh and Glasgow), unless habitats are those clearly avoided by wildcats (see above). For more detailed consideration of habitats (ITE land classes) that show a high association with wildcat presence see Easterbee *et al.* (1991). ITE land classes that wildcats showed a preference for from highest to lowest are: varied lowland margins with heterogeneous land use (28); margins of high mountains and moorlands, often afforested (22); upper valley slopes, mainly covered with bogs (21); smooth hills, mainly heather moors, often afforested (19); and rounded hills, some steep slopes, varied moorlands (18); but land class 22 is most abundant throughout northern Scotland. The presence of rabbit warrens in these habitats may also be a positive sign for the potential presence of wildcats. It may also be worth consulting local people, especially gamekeepers and farmers, to see if they have seen wildcats in an area, owing to the highly secretive behaviour of wildcats, which are likely to be seen only rarely by chance. Local museums may have specimen records indicating historic and recent distribution of wildcats.

### General survey

An initial walk-through survey can establish which sites may serve as breeding dens, including hollow trees, among tree roots, dense scrub, peat haggs, rock crevices, scree fields, old mines, cairns, boulders, rabbit burrows, disused badger setts, fox earths and under fallen debris. Den sites are usually marked by urine sprays, which may have a strong smell, and possibly scats, and the presence of prey in dens or prey remains outside, e.g. rabbit fur and bones, may be a useful indicator. More generally within an area, signs that may indicate the presence of wildcats are urine sprays and scats on prominent features along tracks and trails, such as logs and rocks, scratch marks on tree trunks and paw prints, which are particularly visible in snow (*Fig. 6.5*). However, it is important to note that the

wildcat is sympatric with feral domestic cats and hybridises readily with them. These signs cannot be reliably distinguished between those of wildcats, domestic cats and their hybrids. Any possible den sites should be noted and mapped for future observation and to inform future decisions.

Surveys are best done in the winter when vegetation is less likely to obscure den sites, and signs and footprints can be seen in snow, or in late summer after breeding dens are vacated. Surveys should also be done well in advance of any land management operations that may disturb wildcats or their dens. It should be noted that it is not possible to confirm with certainty whether wildcats are present or not by this methodology, although it can indicate the potential for wildcat presence. To confirm the presence of wildcats, camera trapping is necessary (see protocol below).

### Detailed survey

If a preliminary survey reveals possible den sites, a follow-up detailed survey should be carried out to try to determine whether a den site is being used. This may take several days or even several weeks, depending on the survey area and numbers of cats. Direct observation of cats is ideal and identification should follow the pelage criteria (*Figs. 6.6* and *6.7*) established by Kitchener *et al.* (2005). The relaxed definition is recommended at this stage based on the precautionary principle, because it may be difficult to see all wildcat pelage characteristics in the field. In other words, any large, striped, tabby cat with a bushy, striped, blunt, black-tipped tail should be regarded as probably being a wildcat.

Given the difficulties and cost of repeated surveys to establish direct observations, camera traps offer a much more cost- and time-effective method to detect the presence of wildcats. In combination with food or scent baits as attractants, the presence of wildcats could be established in an area much more quickly and reliably. Kilshaw & Macdonald (2011) have established a camera-trap methodology for surveying wildcats in the field (*Fig. 6.8*). They recommend at least 20 camera trap stations placed no more than 1 km apart with two cameras at each. These should be run for two months and baited to improve trapping success rate. Cameras should be placed 3–6 m away from and perpendicular to the bait at 30–80 cm high (depending on the topography of the ground) and angled slightly to try to photograph the dorsal stripe, which is a key diagnostic pelage character. If no bait is used, the cameras at each station should be 8–10 m apart, because if they are too close or too far apart, the photographs will not be good enough. Baits may include scent such as valerian and catnip, but be aware that not all cats

[7] http://www.searchnbn.net/searchengine/search.jsp?tab=1&pg=1&searchTerm=Wildcat

[8] http://www.brisc.org.uk/Sources.php

[9] http://www.snh.gov.uk/

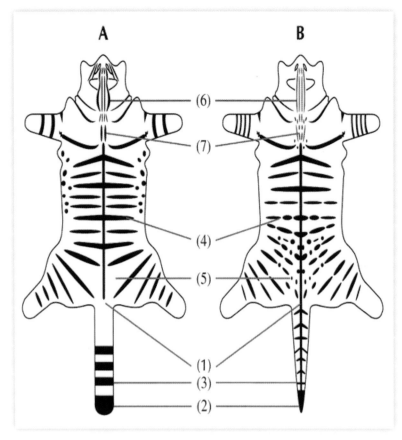

*Figure 6.7.* **Key pelage characters that distinguish a Scottish wildcat (left) from a domestic tabby cat (right).**

Seven Key Pelage Characters: (1) Extent of dorsal line; (2) Shape of tail tip; (3) Distinctness of tail bands; (4) Broken stripes on flanks; (5) Spots on hindquarters; (6) Shape and number of stripes on nape; (7) Shape and number of stripes on the shoulders.

[from Kitchener *et al.* 2005].

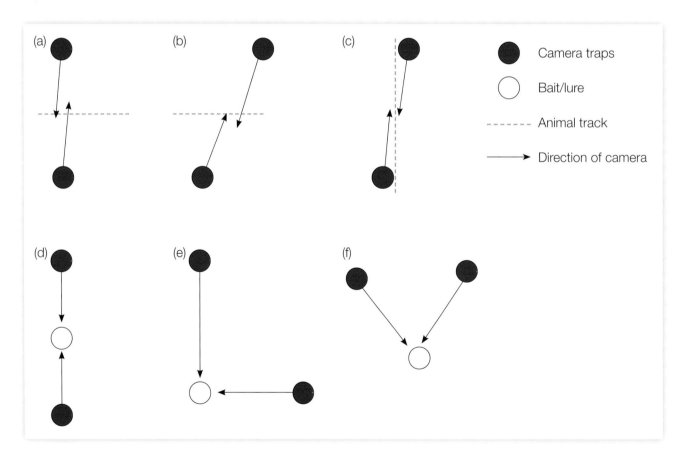

*Figure 6.8.* **A camera-trap methodology for surveying wildcats in the field.**

Main camera trap layouts used for survey without bait (a, b and c) and with bait or lure attached to either a tree or post (d, e and f).

[from Kilshaw & Macdonald 2011].

are able to detect this, or food, such as pheasants or rabbits. Pheasant wings were found to be particularly effective attractors (K. Kilshaw, *pers. comm.*). A licence from SNH may be required for camera trapping of suspected den sites, if there is the possibility of any disturbance.

In the absence of camera traps, it may be possible to extract DNA from scats or hairs. The Royal Zoological Society of Scotland's Zoo Genetics Lab is able to confirm whether any DNA successfully extracted may be of wildcat origin. However, it should be noted that correlation between the pelage criteria of Kitchener *et al.* (2005) and the genetic markers of Driscoll *et al.* (2007) has not been fully confirmed for mtDNA – see Kilshaw *et al.* (2010) – although the results so far are highly encouraging.

## 6.7. Impact Assessment, Mitigation, Compensation and Enhancement

Any project may disturb wildcats and their den sites, so that surveys are required before any actions can be taken in any area where wildcats are likely to occur. Activities that are likely to impact on wildcats, owing to disturbance, direct mortality or fragmentation of habitats, include roads and road building, forestry, quarrying and mineral extraction, house and industrial site building, wind farms, etc. Although the potential effects of projects on wildcats has been considered in recent years in EIAs, none has been identified as having a significant impact on local wildcat populations, possibly because there is insufficient information about and relevant criteria for assessing what constitutes a significant impact. For example, loss of a den site may or may not have an impact, depending on whether an individual wildcat has alternative den sites and whether any of these are important for breeding. Given that wildcat home ranges may reach 18 km², an assessment of the impact of any project should be based upon an understanding of the wildcat's needs at a landscape scale. The risk is that without clear criteria for assessing impact at this level, there will be a continual erosion of the quality of wildcat habitats by incremental developments, which separately may not be considered damaging to local wildcat populations. In the meantime, a precautionary approach is required. Given that only a few hundred wildcats exist in Scotland, any developments which increase the risk of mortality to this species could potentially have a significant impact on the conservation status of populations at the national level. On this basis, methods should always be sought to avoid, reduce or mitigate potential impacts.

Below is a brief review of the kinds of mitigation that have been developed or suggested based on studies and developments undertaken in Scotland and elsewhere in Europe.

### Road traffic accidents

Wildcats are highly likely to be killed in road traffic accidents. Indeed recent surveys have relied heavily on road casualties for direct examination of animals to assess populations (Easterbee *et al.* 1991; Balharry & Daniels 1998; Davis & Gray 2010). Therefore, roads may have direct impacts on local populations by killing, but they may also lead to fragmentation of habitats by wildcats avoiding roads owing to heavy levels of traffic. Mitigation has centred on allowing wildcats safe passage across roads to minimise mortality and maximise connectivity of habitats.

Studies in Spain and Portugal have focused on the use of culverts under roads and railways by terrestrial vertebrates, but many of these studies have found that wildcats do not use them even though present in an area (Ascensão & Mira 2007; Grilo *et al.* 2008; Yanes *et al.* 1995). However, Rodriguez *et al.* (1996; 1997) found that wildcats and other medium-sized carnivores did use culverts, ranging from 1.2 to 3.5 m wide, and that close proximity of appropriate habitat to culvert entrances was important in encouraging their usage. In Germany 0.4 wildcat kills per km per year were recorded on a motorway used by 10,000 vehicles/day and fenced with a regular wildlife fence (Klar *et al.* 2009). By using wildcat-specific exclusion fencing, this rate was reduced by 83 %. Wildcat-specific fences used on the A60 in Germany since 2001 consist of 2 m high, 5 cm x 5 cm mesh fences with a 50 cm steel sheet overhang and a 30 cm deep plastic panel, which was buried in the soil to prevent digging (*Fig. 6.9*). It was designed by Landesbetrieb Mobilität Rheinland-Pfalz, Koblenz, Germany. Wildcats prefer to use very wide (335+ m) open-span viaducts to cross roads, but individuals also showed preferences for particular underpasses and would take detours of > 1 km to use their preferred crossing place. Wildcats often showed hesitancy when approaching crossing structures and were often deterred, especially by traffic noise, so that some would wait > 200 m away until nightfall, presumably when traffic noise was reduced. Generally wildcats stayed at least 200 m away from roads, but occasionally some hunted or rested nearby. If underpasses are not well designed to funnel wildcats through them, animals may still be killed on roads, because they prefer not to use them compared with overpasses. The wildcat-specific fencing actually provided only a moderate barrier to wildcats. Some individuals were hindered in their daily routine and some stopped crossing completely, but others continued crossing regularly. Klar *et al.* (2009) suggest that wildcat fences with

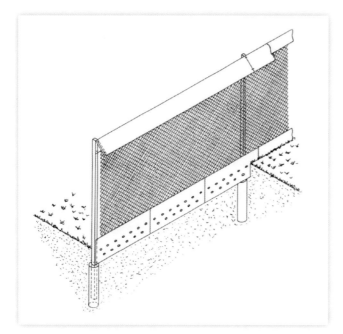

*Figure 6.9.* **Wildcat-specific fencing used on the A60 in Germany since 2001.**

[from Klar *et al.* 2009].

safe crossing structures every 1.5–2.5 km should be employed in road developments, but that the number of roads in a wildcat area should also be minimised to prevent disturbance and mortality. Klar *et al.* (2009) suggested that fences could channel wildcats towards safe crossing places and that these could be made more attractive by ensuring appropriate habitat reached the entrance to the crossing.

Given differences in habitat, road densities, etc., further research is required in Scotland to determine whether wildcats use particular crossing points, whether fences would be effective, and whether wildcats would use culverts (and of what design and location) or other kinds of crossing. The Highways Agency's *Design Manual for Roads and Bridges* (Highways Agency 2001) offers some general advice on mitigation for road developments, which may be useful. Detailed radio-tracking studies are likely to be the only certain way of investigating this problem.

### Loss of or damage to den sites

Den sites are likely to be disturbed, damaged or destroyed during many land management operations, including forestry, quarrying, mining, installation of wind farms, and any building and industrial work that either alters, damages or destroys habitats. If den sites have been located in general and detailed surveys, any work should avoid operations which could damage them or disturb wildcats. Areas within a habitat that are particularly suitable for wildcat dens could be retained as a precautionary measure to prevent damage to potential den sites, even if the presence

of wildcats has not been confirmed. Another option is to avoid any work during the wildcat's breeding season (February–August is ideal to take account of females prospecting for dens in spring and late litters in the summer), which would prevent disturbance of den sites while they are being used. Even if a den is not apparently being used for part of the breeding season, a wildcat may move her kittens there later on in response to potential predators or disturbance at another den site that is being used. Exclusion zones of at least 100 m and preferably of 200 m should be established around potential den sites and other important wildcat areas, such as rabbit warrens, or to maintain habitat corridors. Exclusion zones can be marked to make it clear which areas should be avoided during work operations. However, use of bright tape or other apparently continuous markers should be avoided as this may inhibit or deter wildcats from crossing when out hunting or patrolling their home ranges.

If wildcats are known to be present in an area or strongly suspected and operations would disturb, damage or destroy wildcat den sites, it is essential that a licence is obtained from SNH before commencing work. A licence application requires evidence of the existence of any den sites, that there is no satisfactory alternative to disturbing, damaging or destroying them, and that there will be no detriment to the maintenance of the species at 'favourable conservation status'. Detailed proposals for any mitigation must also be supplied, such as provision of alternative opportunities for den sites (see types and their characteristics above), habitat restoration/corridors, provision of safe road crossings, etc. Licences are only issued for limited reasons, e.g. forestry operations, for reasons of public safety, or overriding public interest, including those of a social or economic nature.

If wildcat activity or signs, or a wildcat den, or evidence of one, are found unexpectedly during work operations, all work must stop immediately and advice should be sought from SNH. This applies also to where accidental damage has been done to a den site during any work. In these cases it is important to record any incidents and the action taken when wildcats or their dens are encountered during any work operations. As well as reviewing any work plans, SNH will probably advise that further survey work should be carried out to try to confirm the presence of wildcats or their den sites. If the presence of wildcats or their dens is subsequently confirmed and the area cannot be avoided, a licence must be applied for from SNH. This licence will almost certainly contain strict conditions, which must be followed closely.

### Habitat loss and fragmentation

Loss of habitat can occur in two ways. Firstly, habitats may change over time so that they become unsuitable for wildcats and their prey. When forestry plantations reach closed-canopy stage, ground-level plants cannot grow, thus eliminating habitat for small mammals such as mice and voles. The solution is to encourage mixed-age and mixed-species forestry, which provides good habitat for wildcats and their prey. Secondly, developments may directly destroy or fragment habitats. For example, housing, industry and intensive agriculture provide no suitable habitat for wildcats, and these and upgrading of roads, resulting in an increase of traffic, may cause fragmentation of habitats. It is vital that regional development plans take into account the habitat needs of wildcats at the landscape level and, if necessary, that habitat corridors are provided to ensure gene flow between wildcat populations in habitat fragments.

### Hybridisation

Introgressive hybridisation with feral domestic cats and hybrid cats is probably the greatest threat to wildcats, which could lead perhaps to their extinction. However, little is known about the process and dynamics of hybridisation, so that a precautionary approach should be employed. Neutering of all domestic cats and hybrids within the wildcat's distribution would eliminate the potential for hybridisation, but it could be difficult to ensure and impractical to carry out nationally. Not all owners would agree to this and at this time it is difficult to envisage legislation to enforce it. There is also no precedent for conditions on new housing developments, which would either preclude the keeping of domestic cats or enforce their neutering, but the feasibility of such an approach could be explored with planning departments.

## 6.8. Research Requirements

Key research requirements include:

- criteria for assessing the effects of projects at the landscape level on the ability of wildcats to withstand incremental losses of parts of their home ranges;

- camera-trap survey of Scotland to assess where populations of wildcats still survive to provide a better understanding of habitat requirements, causes of hybridisation and potential future impacts of major developments, such as wind farms and upgrading the A9 to dual carriageway;

- investigation of the road-crossing behaviour of wildcats and the kinds of mitigation that might be effective in reducing mortality, e.g. culverts, fences, etc.;

- the development of reliable molecular markers for the rapid identification of wildcats in the field and forensically;

- investigation of the process and dynamics of hybridisation with feral domestic cats and hybrids;

- a comparison of trap-neuter-release and culling of feral domestic cats and hybrids on the ability of wildcat populations to recover.

## 6.9. References and Bibliography

Ascensão, F. & Mira, A. (2007) Factors affecting culvert use by vertebrates along two stretches of road in southern Portugal. *Ecological Research* **22**: 57–66.

Balharry, D. & Daniels, M. J. (1998) *Wild-living cats in Scotland*. SNH Research, *Survey and Monitoring Report* **No. 23**. SNH, Edinburgh.

Davis, A. R. & Gray, D. (2010) The distribution of Scottish wildcats (*Felis silvestris*) in Scotland (2006–2008). *Scottish Natural Heritage Commissioned Report* **No. 360**. SNH, Edinburgh.

Driscoll, C. A., Menotti-Raymond, M., Roca, A. L., Hupe, K., Johnson, W. E., Geffen, E., Harley, E. H., Delibes, M., Pontier, D., Kitchener, A. C., Yamaguchi, N., O'Brien, S. J. & Macdonald, D. W. (2007) The near eastern origin of cat domestication. *Science* **317**: 519–523.

Easterbee, N., Hepburn, L. V. & Jefferies D. J. (1991) *Survey of the status and distribution of the wildcat in Scotland, 1983–87*. Nature Conservancy Council for Scotland, Edinburgh.

FCS (2009) *Forest operations and wildcats in Scotland*. FCS Guidance Note 35d. (http://www.forestry.gov.uk/pdf/EPSWildcat.pdf/$FILE/EPSWildcat.pdf).

Grilo, C., Bissonette, J. A. & Santos-Reis, M. (2008) Response of carnivores to existing highway culverts and underpasses: implications for road planning and mitigation. *Biodiversity Conservation* **17**: 1685–1699.

Harris, S., Morris, P. A., Wray, S. & Yalden, D. W. (1995) *A review of British mammals: population estimates and conservation status of British mammals other than cetaceans*. Joint Nature Conservation Committee, Peterborough.

Highways Agency (2001) *Design Manual for Roads and Bridges (DMRB)*. Vol. 10. *Environmental Design and Management*. Section 4. *Nature Conservation*. Part 4 HA81/99 (http://www.dft.gov.uk/ha/standards/dmrb/vol10/section4.htm) and Section 5. *Design for Environmental Barriers* HA 65/94 (http://www.dft.gov.uk/ha/standards/dmrb/vol10/section5.htm).

Jerosch, S., Götz, M., Klar, N. & Roth, M. (2010) Characteristics of diurnal resting sites of the endangered European wildcat (*Felis silvestris silvestris*): Implications for its conservation. *Journal for Nature Conservation* **18**: 45–54.

Kilshaw, K., Drake, A., Macdonald, D W. & Kitchener, A. C. (2010) The Scottish wildcat: a comparison of genetic and pelage characteristics. *Scottish Natural Heritage Commissioned Report* **No. 356**.

Kilshaw, K. & Macdonald, D. W. (2011) The use of camera trapping as a method to survey for the Scottish wildcat. *Scottish Natural Heritage Commissioned Report* **No. 479**. SNH, Edinburgh.

Kitchener, A. (1995) *The Wildcat*. The Mammal Society, London.

Kitchener, A C. (1998) The Scottish wildcat – a cat with an identity crisis? *British Wildlife* **9**: 232–242.

Kitchener, A. C. & Daniels, M. J. (2008) Wildcat *Felis silvestris.* In: Harris, S. & Yalden, D. W. (eds). *Mammals of the British Isles: Handbook,* 4th edition pp 397–406. The Mammal Society, Southampton.

Kitchener, A. C., Yamaguchi, N., Ward, J. M. & Macdonald, D.W. (2005) A diagnosis for the Scottish wildcat: a tool for conservation action for a critically-endangered felid. *Animal Conservation* **8**: 223–237.

Klar, N., Herrmann, M. & Kramer-Schadt, S. (2009) Effects and mitigation of road impacts on individual movement behavior of wildcats. *Journal of Wildlife Management* **73**: 631–638.

Rodriguez, A., Crema, G. & Delibes, M. (1996) Use of non-wildlife passages across a high speed railway by terrestrial vertebrates. *Journal of Applied Ecology* **33**: 1527–1540.

Rodriguez, A., Crema, G. & Delibes, M. (1997) Factors affecting crossing of red foxes and wildcats through nonwildlife passages across a high-speed railway. *Ecography* **20**: 287–294.

SNH (2007) *A Five Year Species Action Framework: Making a difference for Scotland's species*. Scottish Natural Heritage, Perth.

Stahl, P. & Leger, F. (1992) *Le chat sauvage d'Europe (*Felis silvestris *Schreber, 1777)*. Encyclopédie des carnivores de France No. 17. SFEPM, Nort s/Edre.

Yanes, M., Velasco, J. M. & Suárez, F. (1995) Permeability of roads and railways to vertebrates: The importance of culverts. *Biological Conservation* **71**: 217–222.

## Acknowledgements

*The author would like to thank Kerry Kilshaw and Adrian Davis for discussions about surveying for wildcats in the wild. The author is grateful to David Hetherington for his help in sourcing photographs, and also to Nina Klar, for permission to reproduce the figure showing wildcat-specific fencing, and to Keith Baxby, Neville Buck, Kerry Kilshaw, Will Boyd-Wallis and National Museums Scotland for permission to reproduce their photographs.*

# Pine Marten

*Figure 7.1.* Male pine marten in winter pelage.
[Frank Greenaway/The Vincent Wildlife Trust].

# 7. Pine Marten

*By Johnny Birks*

## 7.1. Background Biology

The pine marten *Martes martes* (*Fig. 7.1*) is a medium-sized member of the weasel family, averaging about 74 cm in length and weighing 1.3–1.9 kg. About the size of a slender domestic cat, the pine marten has rich brown fur, a long bushy tail and a striking creamy chest patch or 'bib'. Prominent, rounded, pale-fringed ears and a pointed snout give it an attractive, heart-shaped face. With proportionately longer legs than its close relatives, the pine marten is exceptionally good at climbing to find food, to access elevated resting sites and to escape from danger. Pine martens are opportunist omnivores, taking a wide range of food that varies in line with its changing seasonal and geographical availability. Typically the diet is dominated by small mammals, birds, invertebrates and fruit, but many other foods may feature, including reptiles, lagomorphs and the carrion of larger mammals such as deer. In Britain there is much overlap between the diets of pine martens, foxes *Vulpes vulpes* and wild-living cats such as the Scottish wildcat *Felis silvestris* (Balharry *et al*. 2008).

Pine martens are mainly solitary, though the home ranges of males and females tend to overlap; males occupy home ranges approximately twice the size of those of females. Home range size varies according to the extent and quality of suitable habitat available. In poor quality upland habitat with highly fragmented woodland cover (such as in the Scottish Highlands), average home range size may exceed 20 km$^2$ for males and 8 km$^2$ for females. Conversely in prey-rich, lowland woodland home ranges of both sexes may be less than 2 km$^2$. In Scottish commercial mixed conifer plantations home ranges are typically 3–9 km$^2$ for males and 2–5 km$^2$ for females. The animals are predominantly nocturnal in winter; in summer up to half of all activity occurs during daylight, but diurnal activity is usually confined to thick cover (Balharry *et al*. 2008).

Pine martens are slow breeders, with one small litter per year (average litter size of three, though in poor habitat litters of just one or two are common). Slow maturation and a lengthy delayed implantation means that young females typically give birth first when they are three years old. The cubs or kits are usually born in March/April in an elevated and well-insulated natal den such as a hollow tree. Where such sites are absent, female martens may give birth in owl boxes or the roofs of houses (Birks *et al*. 2005). Non-breeding pine martens commonly rest in elevated sites that provide much less shelter than natal dens, such as disused corvid or raptor nests, squirrel dreys or, in fine weather, on exposed tree branches. Some young martens disperse in the autumn following their birth, but animals of pre-breeding age may be tolerated by other adults, so some may disperse later. Pine martens may live for well over ten years in the wild (Balharry *et al*. 2008).

Pine martens are vulnerable to a wide range of predators. In the past, predator control by humans had a serious adverse effect upon pine marten conservation status in the UK. Populations are recovering now, but human intolerance remains a concern in some areas. Unlike some of their close relatives, such as the polecat *Mustela putorius*, pine martens do not produce pungent anal gland secretions to mount an effective 'stink defence', relying instead on their ability to climb away from danger. Significant wild predators include the red fox and golden eagle *Aquila chrysaetos*; predator avoidance exerts a big influence upon pine marten habitat selection. Studies in Scandinavia suggest that predation by foxes is a limiting factor for pine marten populations (Lindström *et al*. 1995).

## 7.2. Habitat Requirements

The pine marten is a wide-ranging habitat specialist that is dependent upon substantial areas with a marked vertical component, such as extensive woodland (*Fig. 7.2*), in which its agility and climbing skills enable it to escape from terrestrial predators such as foxes. Closed canopy woodland also offers protection against aerial predators such as large birds of prey. Woodlands need to be relatively large and well-connected if they are to support a viable population comprising several pine marten home ranges. In order to support a self-sustaining pine marten population, woodland must provide two essential resources: a diverse, year-round food supply; and sufficient elevated denning and resting sites, including suitable natal dens for use by breeding females between March and June. Female pine martens need natal dens that offer shelter against wind and rain, insulation against temperature extremes and elevation above the reach of most predators (Zalewski 1997; Birks *et al*. 2005). Elevated tree cavities (*Fig. 7.3*) provide these resources and so are critical for successful reproduction, especially where foxes are common and the risk of predation at ground level is high. Over most of Europe, in managed woodlands, pine martens commonly breed in nesting chambers created by the black woodpecker *Dryocopus martius*; this crow-sized bird is not established in

*Figure 7.2.* Extensive woodland habitat suitable for pine martens.
[Johnny Birks].

*Figure 7.3.* Elevated tree cavities provide an essential denning resource for pine martens.
[Johnny Birks].

*Figure 7.4.* Woodland and crag habitat suitable for pine martens in North Wales.
[Rob Strachan].

the UK. Where elevated tree cavities are scarce or absent, pine martens may select alternative dens, including owl boxes and the roof voids of houses close to woodland; some elevated den sites offer limited shelter against the weather, such as squirrel dreys, raptor nests and the tangle of branches in areas of windthrow.

Over much of the UK, as a consequence of woodland clearance and frequent harvesting for timber, the extent, distribution, species composition and age structure of woodland habitat is less than ideal for a habitat specialist like the pine marten (Bright 1993). At about 12 % woodland cover (17 % in Scotland), Britain remains one of the most deforested parts of Europe; most woodlands are too small (> 70 % of UK woodlands are less than 10 ha in area) to support a viable pine marten home range, and many are isolated by open farmland; the largest woodland blocks tend to be commercial conifer plantations established in the 20th century, where structural and species diversity are low and elevated arboreal cavities are absent. Even in our ancient semi-natural woodlands the history of 20th century timber harvesting means that, above ground level, most trees are too young to offer many elevated tree cavities suitable for pine martens.

In the absence of extensive woodland, some rocky landscapes (*Fig. 7.4*) offer structural alternatives, with elevated rock crevices substituting for den sites in hollow trees. When woodland cover in Britain fell below 5 % in the late 1800s, pine martens apparently survived mainly in rocky landscapes such as the Scottish north-west Highlands, the Lake District and Snowdonia (e.g. Webster 2001).

Pine martens are mobile animals that are good at dispersing, and this helps them to occupy landscapes in which woodland is fragmented. However, recent studies in France (Pereboom *et al.* 2008) show that pine martens moving through open fields tend to stay within 30 m of woodland or trees in order to escape from predators. This suggests that woodland connectivity involving lines of trees is important to commuting or dispersing pine martens.

## 7.3. Status and Distribution

The pine marten has a highly restricted distribution in the UK (*Fig. 7.5*) following major historical population declines caused by woodland clearance and culling by humans (Balharry *et al.* 2008). The species' nadir in Britain in the early 1900s coincided with the periods of lowest woodland cover and maximum culling pressure on predators associated with game keeping (Langley & Yalden 1977). At the time pine martens survived mainly in the rugged north-west Highlands of Scotland, with smaller refugia further south centred on Lakeland in northern England and Snowdonia in Wales; the species probably survived undetected in other areas of northern England and Wales. In Ireland, where the pine marten's decline occurred rather later than in Britain, its main stronghold was in the rocky west.

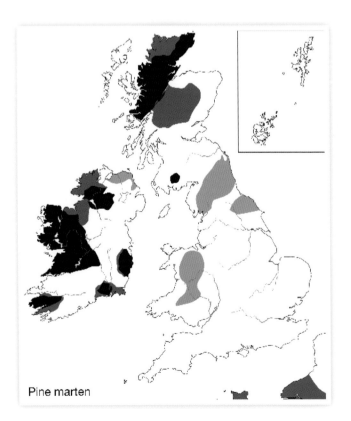

Pine marten

*Figure 7.5.* **The distribution map of pine martens for the British Isles.**

Black indicates regular or usual range; dark grey, scattered but regular occurrence; light grey, rare occurrences, vagrants, or scarce and beyond the regular range. Note that, although there has been no wide scale distribution survey in Scotland since 1994, there is abundant anecdotal evidence that the pine marten's range to the north of the Scottish lowland belt is now considerably more extensive than shown here; also, since construction of the Skye road bridge in 1995, pine martens have begun to colonise the Isle of Skye. [from: Harris & Yalden (2008) *Mammals of the British Isles: Handbook,* 4th edition. Mammal Society; with minor amendments].

Reductions in culling pressure and establishment of new plantation forests in the 20<sup>th</sup> century led to a slow expansion of the pine marten's range in Scotland and Ireland; in England and Wales the very sparse, isolated populations appear to have stagnated at best, though recent surveys suggest long-term persistence of evidence in five core areas. A recent genetic assessment (Jordan *et al. in press*.) suggests that the original relict haplotype found in England and Wales has been mainly replaced by animals of another haplotype now widespread in Scotland. Currently, in Ireland the main stronghold is in the mid-west counties of Mayo, Galway and Clare, with outlier populations in the north (Donegal, Fermanagh and Tyrone), east (Meath, Wicklow and Waterford) and, following a late 20<sup>th</sup> century reintroduction, the south-west (Kerry). Populations are apparently expanding in all these areas (O'Mahony *et al.* 2006). In Scotland, range expansion continues into Aberdeenshire, Moray, Angus, Perth and Kinross, Stirling and Argyll and Bute, with an outlier population re-established in the south-west following a reintroduction to Galloway Forest in the early 1980s. In England and Wales most recent evidence of pine martens comes from areas to the north-west of the Severn–Humber axis: the main concentrations in England are centred on Lakeland, Northumbria and the North York Moors; in Wales the two main concentrations are centred on Snowdonia in the north and Carmarthenshire/Breconshire in the south (Birks & Messenger 2010).

## 7.4. Legislative Protection

Pine martens are fully protected in England and Wales through their inclusion on Schedules 5 and 6 of the Wildlife and Countryside Act 1981. The Act makes it an offence (subject to exceptions) to intentionally kill, injure or take a pine marten, to intentionally or recklessly damage, destroy or obstruct access to places used by pine martens for shelter or protection, or intentionally or recklessly to disturb pine martens occupying such places. There is no provision for licensing development activities under the Wildlife and Countryside Act. In Northern Ireland they receive the same level of protection under the Wildlife (Northern Ireland) Order (1985). In Scotland pine martens receive a similar level of protection under the Wildlife and Countryside Act 1981, as amended by the Nature Conservation (Scotland) Act 2004 and the Wildlife and Natural Environment (Scotland) Act 2011, with the protection extended to include 'reckless' acts (continuing with an action in the knowledge of the consequences of that action) and acts of 'interference', as an addition to destructive acts cited in the 1981 Act.

Although fully protected under UK legislation, the pine marten is not a 'European Protected Species' (it is listed on Schedule 4 of the Conservation of Habitats and Species Regulations 2010 and Schedule 3 of the Conservation (Natural Habitats, &c.) Regulations 1994 (as amended) in Scotland, which relates to animals that may not be captured or killed in certain ways).

The pine marten also receives protection in England and Wales under the Natural Environment and Rural Communities Act (2006) requiring all public bodies to have regard for biodiversity conservation.

## 7.5. Summary of UK BAP Status and Recommended Actions

The pine marten was listed in 2007 as a priority species for conservation in the UK BAP, and is on the Biodiversity Lists for England and Wales (listed as a Species of Principal Importance under the NERC Act, 2006), and Northern Ireland (listed as a Priority Species in the Northern Ireland Priority Species List, March 2010).

The BAP recommended actions for the pine marten are (http://jncc.defra.gov.uk/_speciespages/2405.pdf):

- promote strategic reafforestation to increase general woodland cover to > 25 % and improve connectivity in regions where pine martens occur in England and Wales;

- within woodland, increase above-ground den site availability through retention of standing old and damaged trees (long-term action) and through provision of den boxes (short term);

- promote sustainable solutions to conflicts between pine martens and people (e.g. marten predation upon poultry and game, martens breeding in roofs of houses);

- develop improved methods for detecting pine martens where populations are sparse;

- predict range expansion for all populations based on present and future habitat availability;

- consider reintroductions into areas where there are no extant populations and where there is (or will be) suitable habitat to support self-sustaining populations.

## 7.6. Survey Methodology

The type and extent of survey that is appropriate in each case will be dependent on the purposes of the survey. In some cases a survey may look to answer several questions, and a number of different survey types may be carried out at the same time. In the majority of cases where a survey is required, it will be appropriate to collect information using a combination of desk study and field survey.

### Establishing the presence of pine martens

It may be appropriate to undertake a survey to

confirm the presence of pine martens in a particular area, which can be done in various ways (see below). However, it can be difficult to confirm absence of pine martens on the basis of a survey where no evidence is recorded. In this case the survey would need to be set against the context of a desk study. Indeed, a desk study may establish the presence of pine martens in an area, making it unnecessary to undertake a field survey. A range of information sources should be used to inform the desk study, including local Biodiversity Records Centre available data, records held by the local Biodiversity Action Plan and the NBN gateway website; in the case of sites in England or Wales, The Vincent Wildlife Trust (VWT) should be approached for records of pine martens.

Pine martens are wide-ranging animals that may occupy large home ranges. Therefore a search radius of 5 km around a development site should normally be used during the desk study; in upland landscapes where home ranges are typically much larger, a search radius of 10 km is more appropriate. Depending on the nature and extent of any project, any recent (≤ 10 years) pine marten record within 2 km (5 km in upland landscapes) should trigger the need for a field survey. Critical projects are those that might adversely affect the ability of pine martens to maintain populations within, or disperse between, areas of suitable habitat (e.g. woodland and rugged uplands). So any change affecting > 50 ha of suitable habitat,

or a less extensive change resulting in the removal or severance of dispersal routes between habitat blocks, should trigger the need for a field survey.

Where a field survey is required to determine pine marten presence, the most appropriate approach will be determined by the questions to be answered and the survey's resources and timescale. The following non-intrusive survey and detection options are available.

### Passive sign surveys

Passive field sign surveys are based upon searching in suitable habitat for pine marten footprints and droppings (called scats). The five-toed, slightly cat-like footprints (up to 65 mm wide in males) are not always distinctive, and because pine martens tend to avoid mud this field sign is not widely available in the absence of extensive snow cover (**Fig. 7.6**). However, at sites where good winter snow cover can be relied upon, transects to detect pine marten footprints should be walked and all possible footprints photographed with an accompanying scale.

Pine marten scats (**Fig. 7.7**) are highly variable in size and shape depending upon their contents; typically 4–12 cm long and 0.8–1.8 cm in diameter, they have a slightly sweet smell when fresh. Where a pine marten population is well established, with contiguous or overlapping territories occupying all available habitat, individuals tend to communicate and defend their territories by depositing some of their scats on pathways through woodland and on prominent objects such as rocks and fallen trees. Therefore, systematic searches for scats along transects, following paths, rides and track ways through woodland or rocky habitats, offer one simple means of determining pine marten presence (Birks *et al.* 2004). The number and length of transects should be determined by the extent of the survey area, the extent of pine marten habitat and the availability of suitable transect routes (e.g. paths and woodland rides). As a general rule, transects should be a standard length of 1 or 2 km and transect density should comprise no less than 5 per hectad (10 x 10 km square) of suitable habitat; in well-wooded hectads at least 10 transects should be completed.

There are some important caveats to note when using the scat survey approach.

In areas where populations are sparse and territorial defence is relatively unimportant, scat searches may fail to detect pine marten presence simply because the animals are less likely to deposit their scats as territory markers; in such situations most scats are probably deposited at den sites and in foraging areas. If this is likely to be the case, another survey method should be used.

Even where pine marten populations are well-

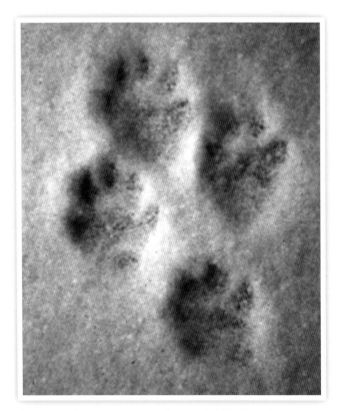

*Figure 7.6.* **Pine marten tracks in snow, Kielder Forest, Northumberland.**
[Rob Strachan].

*Figure 7.7.* Pine marten scats.
[Lizzie Croose; Johnny Birks].

*Figure 7.8.* Tree-mounted hair tubes (above) with visiting marten showing the sticky pad (below) with a hair sample attached.
[Peter Turner and Lizzie Croose].

established, there are marked seasonal variations in the abundance of scats detected on survey transects. In one Scottish study scat abundance in mid-winter was 100 times lower than in late summer (Velander 1983); so scat surveys should be conducted in the period May to September inclusive (ideally June to August) when the chances of encountering scats are highest.

Where surveys have to be conducted in mid-winter, another survey method should be used.

Carnivore scats are not distinctive, so identification errors may occur. There is overlap in the size and morphology of pine marten scats and the faeces of other species, so DNA typing of scats is essential to confirm pine marten presence (Davison *et al.* 2002); this is now a standard element of pine marten scat surveys. All possible pine marten scats should be collected and individually bagged and labelled using methods that avoid the risk of cross-contamination of DNA samples.

### Hair tubes

Tree-mounted hair tubes (*Fig. 7.8*) made of 250 mm sections of 118 mm diameter standard sewage pipe, incorporating sticky pads at the base and bait at the top, have been developed by Peter Turner of Waterford Institute of Technology [10] as a cost-effective method of collecting hair samples from free-ranging pine martens (Mullins *et al.* 2009). Hairs collected by the sticky pads can be identified by microscopy or DNA analysis of follicles. The latter technique also allows identification of individual pine martens, so may be used to undertake a population census. The 'Turner Tube' technique works well in relatively high-density pine marten populations where the survey can run for a few weeks to allow time for target animals to detect and visit the tubes; it may fail where the animals are scarce.

### Camera traps

Digital 'camera traps' focused on elevated baiting stations (e.g. a platform in a tree) may be used to detect pine martens at sites where there is sufficient time to set cameras up for several weeks (*Fig. 7.9*). Ideally cameras should use infrared flash (rather than daylight flash) and bait should be fresh meat, peanut butter and/or fruit, replenished at least weekly. Although non-target terrestrial species may be avoided by elevating the bait station, there may still be visits from squirrels, small rodents and birds such as raptors and corvids. In common with other detection methods this approach may fail where pine martens are scarce.

### Footprint tunnels

A footprint recording system first developed in New Zealand for detecting small mustelids has been successfully adapted by R. C. Trout [11] for use on pine martens. The method relies upon the animals' readiness to explore artificial tunnels (made of lightweight plastic shrub guards 120 mm long x 17 cm diameter) in which is placed a tracking board supporting a central ink pad with strips of pre-treated paper either side of the pad. As an animal passes through the tunnel, the 'ink' picked up on its feet reacts with the paper to produce an indelible dye (*Fig. 7.10*). Footprint tunnels should be visited weekly to replenish 'ink' and replace papers. In common with other detection methods, this approach may fail where pine martens are scarce.

### Assessing habitat quality and identifying features of particular significance, such as den sites

In relation to many projects, in order to assess impacts it will be important to categorise the habitat available to pine martens and to identify locations of denning or breeding sites within the area of the works, or sufficiently close for animals using them to be disturbed or indirectly affected.

### General habitat assessment

A landscape-scale approach based upon scoring each monad (1 x 1 km square) of the National Ordnance Survey Grid in and around a study site is appropriate for assessing general habitat suitability for pine martens; because of the relatively large home ranges occupied by pine martens, it is appropriate also to assess habitat within each monad occupying a 5 km buffer zone around the periphery of any development site. A simple scoring system that quantifies a series of key features on a scale of 1 to 3 can be combined to score each monad as 'high', 'medium' or 'low' quality for pine martens. This approach concentrates on assessment of the presence and quality/extent/abundance of each feature under four main headings: the foraging resource; the extent and connectivity of suitable habitat; the availability of elevated denning and resting sites; and potential mortality factors. Such an assessment may be completed for most sites through a combination of field survey and examination of maps and aerial photographs. Note that monads with overall 'medium' or 'high' habitat suitability scores are likely to be suitable for pine martens, so should trigger the need for mitigation and/or compensation if significant impacts are predicted during EcIA. The key features identified under the four main categories are shown in *Table 7.1* (note that the mortality factors involve a negative score).

---

[10] pturner@wit.ie

[11] rabbitwise@hotmail.co.uk

*Figure 7.9.* A digital 'camera trap'.
[Johnny Birks].

*Figure 7.10.* Pine marten ink pad footprints from a footprint tunnel.
[Roger Trout].

*Identification of potential den sites*

This will require surveys of all suitable habitat to determine whether or not potential den sites are present, such as elevated tree cavities, roof voids of buildings or barns within or close to woodland, owl boxes, large raptor or corvid nests, squirrel dreys and rocky outcrops with elevated crevices; in blocks of commercial forestry the presence of windthrow offering an elevated tangle of branches and large uplifted rootplates may provide den sites.

Current or recent use of den sites by pine martens may be revealed by the presence of accumulations of scats beneath den entrances (though an absence of scats is not reliable evidence of non-use). Natal dens in particular may have substantial piles of fresh scats beneath them (or on top of them in the case of owl and marten boxes) during the period March–June.

Pine martens may use different sites at different times of year. For example, the most sheltered den sites may be most heavily used by breeding females in summer and then by adults in winter when the weather is poor; in summer, in fine weather, pine martens may simply rest up trees on branches. It would be appropriate to repeat resting site surveys at different times of year, where potential den sites exist but no evidence of use was recorded on the initial survey.

Close investigation of structures for evidence of use by pine martens may require a surveyor to cause significant disturbance (using a torch or a fibrescope), and may therefore need to take place under a licence from the relevant SNCO (see Section 1.6).

In general, examinations of the area around the entrance of such structures do not require a survey licence in England and Scotland. However, internal examination (such as use of a fibrescope) or prolonged monitoring may also need to be undertaken under licence within any part of the UK. The relevant SNCO should be contacted for country-specific advice.

The area of survey for resting sites will be dependent upon the type of development and the extent of the potential impacts. Surveys up to 250 m beyond the extent of the works may be required for construction activities likely to generate a significant level of noise or visual disturbance. Less intrusive activities, such as construction, extension or renovation of a single small building (e.g. a dwelling house) within or adjacent to woodland where pine martens are known to be present, would require a less extensive survey of circa 50–100 m around the area of works.

## 7.7. Impact Assessment, Mitigation, Compensation and Enhancement

### Impact assessment

*Habitat loss or loss of key features*

Projects that involve the permanent loss of significant areas of woodland, the severance of tree lines and other connecting features (e.g. stone walls) linking woodland blocks, or the loss of elevated den sites, may have a significant adverse impact upon pine marten populations. The relative importance of such impacts would depend upon

*Table 7.1.* Habitat assessment scoring for pine martens.

| Category | Feature | Subjective score based upon presence/ abundance of each feature in a monad |
|---|---|---|
| Foraging resource | Abundance of fruit-bearing trees and shrubs.<br>Extent of rough grassland/pre-thicket plantations (vole populations).<br>Extent of mature conifers with well-developed field layer.<br>Area of broadleaf woodland and scrub.<br>Extent of tree-lined stream valleys and wetlands.<br>Rabbit abundance. | 1 to 3, where 1 = poor and 3 = rich foraging resource. |
| Habitat extent and connectivity | Extent of 3-dimensional habitat (e.g. woodland) in target monad and surrounding monads.<br>Habitat connectivity by hedges or tree lines beyond woodland edge. | 1 to 3, where 1 = poor and 3 = good habitat extent and connectivity. |
| Den availability | Abundance of potential elevated den sites (e.g. over-mature trees with cavities, windthrow, squirrel dreys, raptor or corvid nests, owl boxes, rock outcrops). | 1 to 3, where 1 = poor and 3 = good den availability. |
| Mortality risk factors | Evidence of predator control (e.g. tunnel traps around pheasant pens).<br>Fox abundance.<br>Density of main roads in target monad and surrounding monads. | -1 to -3, where -1 = low and -3 = high mortality risk. |
| Total | | Sum scores for each monad. Possible scores for each monad will range between 0 and 8, where score 0–2 = low, 3–5 = medium, and 6-8 = high habitat suitability. |

the scale of habitat loss and the size of the pine marten population affected. However, given the large home range size, such developments are unlikely to affect more than a small, localised population. Where such habitat loss occurs at the edge of the pine marten's range this could be more significant, potentially at the Regional level. However, because of the general presumption in planning decisions in favour of retaining woodland, in most cases development projects will not give rise to sufficiently large habitat losses to have a significant adverse effect on pine martens. Therefore, impacts will mainly be confined to issues of habitat connectivity and loss of den sites. The significance of any such losses will need to be determined on a case-by-case basis. It should be noted that damage or destruction of a pine marten resting site is an offence under current legislation, and the appropriate approach in such circumstances would need to be discussed with the relevant SNCO.

### Habitat fragmentation

The adverse effects upon wildlife dispersal of the construction of transport corridors and other significant barriers are well known. The pine marten is especially vulnerable to habitat fragmentation because each individual requires a large home range, ideally comprising contiguous woodland or well-connected woodland blocks. Bisection of a large woodland block by linear development may destroy the viability of one or more pine marten home ranges. The development of land between woodland blocks may destroy important commuting routes and so may also undermine the viability of individual home ranges. These local effects, together with wider effects upon dispersal routes, may impact adversely upon pine marten populations. Again, these impacts are likely to be significant only at a Local level, unless they include very long routes through strongholds of the species.

### Mortality of animals

Pine martens are increasingly killed by traffic while crossing roads (*Fig. 7.11*), particularly in parts of Scotland where populations are recovering. Therefore, new road schemes and other transport routes should be assessed for their likely impact upon pine marten populations, especially where they are routed through or near to blocks of woodland habitat between which pine martens are likely to commute.

Significant mortality may also arise from the non-target effects of some forms of pest control, such as the use of lethal tunnel traps to control ground predators in areas where game or poultry are kept, and the use of poisons to control grey squirrels in commercial forestry. Any developments in areas occupied by pine martens should be assessed for

their likely impact upon such sources of mortality. Mortality during woodland clearance or forestry operations is a possibility, especially during the period March to June when breeding females and/or their young are confined to elevated natal den sites in arboreal cavities.

### Disturbance

Pine martens are generally tolerant of most forms of human disturbance that do not directly threaten their safety. Therefore, the carefully-planned introduction into woodland occupied by pine martens of certain daytime recreational activities, such as well-directed cycle routes, need not lead to significant disturbance post-development (nocturnal human activities may be more disturbing because they coincide with the main period when animals are active and foraging in their home ranges). The use of upland woodlands for wind energy generation may have minimal post-development disturbance impacts upon resident pine martens (though there may be significant disturbance impacts during construction, and other adverse habitat impacts may arise from tree felling and the provision of infrastructure). Even the introduction of low density holiday accommodation into woodland may not involve long-term disturbance; indeed in Scotland and Ireland pine martens increasingly breed in the roofs of occupied houses where natural tree cavities are rare or absent in local woodlands.

An important caveat in all development, however, is the need to recognise the adverse impact of disturbance to animals using resting and breeding sites, and the legal implications of such disturbance. For developments within or close to woodland, such impacts are likely to be most serious where the development phase occurs during the pine marten breeding season (March to June). Therefore, impact assessment should concentrate upon two key aspects of disturbance: the extent to which pine martens occupying dens (and breeding dens in particular) may be disturbed during development; and the extent to which any post-development activities may lead to disturbance to pine martens, whether while resting at dens or active elsewhere in their home ranges.

### Mitigation and compensation

Any significant habitat losses will need to be mitigated and compensated for through the creation of replacement features, such as establishing new areas of woodland and creating new tree lines to restore safe commuting routes between woodland blocks, provision of 'green bridges' or aerial crossing routes over transport corridors, and provision of artificial dens to compensate for the loss of existing or potential den sites.

*Figure 7.11.* A pine marten road mortality.
[Cresswell].

*Figure 7.12.* A pine marten aerial crossing over a road in the Netherlands.
[Jaap Mulder].

*New woodland*

The design and location of new woodlands within a development project may be critical to achieving effective mitigation and compensation efforts for pine martens. While it may take many decades before new woodlands provide all the resources required by pine martens (such as elevated tree cavities), good foraging habitat and safe commuting routes may develop within a few years after planting. The mix of species planted should include native fruit- and nut-bearing trees and shrubs. The design plan should incorporate glades and wide rides to provide open foraging areas, and new woodlands should be fitted thoughtfully into the landscape so that they improve connectivity to existing woodlands; linear 'linking' woodlands are much more valuable than isolated woodland blocks.

*Road crossings*

New road schemes should consider ways of reducing the likelihood of pine marten mortality as part of their design. Such measures could include the construction of 'green bridges' that will benefit a wide range of mobile wildlife species. To work well for pine martens, such bridges need to support tree cover and must be located intelligently in relation to existing areas of woodland, with new tree plantings used to guide the movements of dispersing and commuting animals. Their unusual ability to climb over obstacles means there is no such thing as pine marten-resistant fencing (unless it is electrified) to guide the animals' movements and prevent them gaining access to roads.

Pine martens are likely to use dry culverts beneath roads, so these should be provided at probable crossing points; where culverts carry streams beneath a road a dry ledge above flood level should be provided for terrestrial animals such as pine martens.

A further way to enable martens to cross roads safely is to make adaptations to existing elevated structures above roads. In the Netherlands, gantries displaying signs for vehicle drivers above motorways bisecting woodland have been modified to provide safe crossings for both martens and squirrels (though there is little evidence that these have been used). At each end of the gantry the elevated supporting metal frame is extended into the trees beside the road; a wooden channel runs along the whole length of the extended gantry, providing a safe route over the road for arboreal mammals (*Fig. 7.12*).

*Artificial dens*

As a short- to medium-term measure, pending the development of natural cavities in standing deadwood, the provision of artificial dens for pine martens is an effective form of mitigation. A purpose-built wooden den box developed and tested by The VWT (*Fig. 7.13*) has proved popular with wild pine martens, including for breeding. Guidance on construction, installation and monitoring of the VWT box are available as free downloads.[12] Note that any checking of den boxes that might involve disturbance to pine martens should be carried out under a licence from the appropriate authority.

*Enhancement*

All development schemes should be aiming to deliver biodiversity enhancements; there are some simple measures that may enhance habitat for pine martens as part of development projects. Notably, two important constraints currently acting upon the favourable conservation status of the species in the UK are: (a) the low and fragmented nature of woodland cover, and (b) the scarcity of elevated tree cavities within woodlands. These two constraints may be eased through carefully-planned new woodland planting and provision of den boxes, as described in the sections above.

## 7.8. Research Requirements

Key research requirements include:

- refinement and testing of protocols for presence-absence surveys and determination of their limits of effectiveness (e.g. scat surveys, footprint tunnels, hair tubes, camera traps);

- assessment of effectiveness of road crossing provision for pine martens (e.g. green bridges, dry culverts);

- development of a Habitat Suitability Index for pine marten;

- development of a protocol for using trained dogs for detecting pine marten scats.

## 7.9. References and Bibliography

Balharry, E. A., McGowan, G. M., Kruuk, H. & Halliwell, E. (1996) Distribution of pine martens in Scotland as determined by field survey and questionnaire. *Scottish Natural Heritage Research, Survey and Monitoring Report* **No. 48**. SNH, Edinburgh.

Balharry, E., Jefferies, D. J. & Birks, J. D. S. (2008) Pine marten. In Harris, S. & Yalden, D. W. (eds) *Mammals of the British Isles: Handbook*, 4th edition, pp 447–455. The Mammal Society, Southampton.

Birks, J. D. S., Braithwaite, A. C., Brookes, R. C. Davison, A. Gough, M. C., Messenger, J. E. & Strachan, C. (2001) Detecting pine martens in England and Wales. In: Birks, J. D. S. & H.J.

---

[12] http://www.vwt.org.uk/downloads.php

*Figure 7.13.* A purpose-built wooden den box for pine martens being installed (left) and occupied (right).
[Johnny Birks/The Vincent Wildlife Trust].

Macmillan (eds) *The Vincent Wildlife Trust Review of 1997–2000* pp 28–30. The Vincent Wildlife Trust.

Birks, J. D. S., Messenger, J. E., Braithwaite, A. C., Davison, A., Brookes, R. C. & Strachan, C. (2004) Are scat surveys a reliable method for assessing distribution and population status of pine martens? In: D. J. Harrison, A. K. Fuller, and G. Proulx (eds). *Marten and Fishers (*Martes*) in Human-altered Environments: An international perspective,* pp 235–252. Kluwer Academic Publishers.

Birks, J. D. S., Messenger, J. E. & Halliwell, E. C. (2005) Diversity of den sites used by pine martens *Martes martes*: a response to the scarcity of arboreal cavities? *Mammal Review* **35**: 313–320.

Birks, J. & Messenger, J. (2010) *Evidence of Pine Martens in England and Wales 1996–2007: Analysis of Reported Sightings and Foundations for the Future*. The Vincent Wildlife Trust.

Bright, P. (1993) Habitat fragmentation – problems and predictions for British mammals. *Mammal Review* **23**: 101–111.

Davison, A., Birks, J. D. S., Brookes, R. C., Braithwaite, A. C. & Messenger J. E. (2002) On the origin of faeces: morphological versus molecular methods for surveying rare carnivores from their scats. *Journal of Zoology (London)* **257**: 141–143.

Jordan, N.R., Messenger, J., Turner, P., Croose, E., Birks, J. & O'Reilly, C. (in press) Molecular comparison of historical and contemporary pine marten (*Martes martes*) populations in the British Isles: evidence of differing origins and fates, and implications for conservation management. **Conservation Genetics.**

Langley, P. J. W. & Yalden, D. W. (1977) The decline of the rarer carnivores in Great Britain during the nineteenth century. *Mammal Review* **7**: 95–116.

Lindström, E. R., Brainerd, S. M., Helldin, J. O. & Overskaug, K. (1995) Pine marten-red fox interactions: a case of intraguild predation? *Annales Zoologici Fennici* **32**: 123–130.

Messenger, J.E., J.D.S. Birks and D.J. Jefferies. (1997) What is the status of the pine marten in England and Wales? *British Wildlife* **8**: 273–279.

Messenger, J. E. & Birks, J. D. S. (2000) Monitoring the very rare: pine marten populations in England and Wales. In: H. I. Griffiths (ed.) *Mustelids in a Modern World. Management and Conservation Aspects of Small Carnivore: Human interactions*. Backhuys.

Messenger, J. E., Birks, J. D. S. & Braithwaite, A. C. (2006) An artificial natal den box for pine martens *Martes martes*. Pages 89-98 *In*: Santos-Reis, M., Birks, J. D. S., O'Doherty E.C. & Proulx,G. (eds) *Martes in Carnivore communities*. Proceedings of the fourth International Martes Symposium, Lisbon, July 2004. Alpha Wildlife Publications.

Mullins, J., Statham, M. J., Roche, T., Turner, P. D. & O'Reilly, C. (2009) Remotely plucked hair genotyping: a reliable and non-invasive method for censusing pine marten (*Martes martes*, L. 1758) populations. *European Journal of Wildlife Research* (published online 17.10.09).

O'Mahony, D., O'Reilly, C. & Turner, P. (2006) *National Pine Marten Survey of Ireland 2005*. http://www.coford.ie/iopen24/pub/COFORD-connects/PineMarten.pdf

O'Sullivan, P. J. (1983) The distribution of the pine marten (*Martes martes*) in the republic of Ireland. *Mammal Review* **13**: 39–44.

Pereboom, V., Mergey, M., Villerette, N., Helder, R., Gerard, J. F. & Lodé, T. (2008) Movement patterns, habitat selection and corridor use of a typical woodland-dweller species, the pine marten (*Martes martes*) in fragmented landscape. *Canadian Journal of Zoology* **86**: 983–991.

Strachan, R., Jefferies, D. J. & Chanin, P. R. F. (1996) *Pine Marten Survey of England and Wales 1987–1988*. Joint Nature Conservation Committee.

Velander, K. A. (1983) *Pine Marten Survey of Scotland, England and Wales 1982–1983*. The Vincent Wildlife Trust.

Webster, J. A. (2001) A review of the historical evidence of the habitat of the pine marten in Cumbria. *Mammal Review* **31**: 17–31.

Zalewski, A. (1997) Factors affecting selection of resting site type by pine marten in primeval deciduous forests (Bialowieża National Park, Poland). *Acta Theriologica* **42** (3): 271–288.

## *Acknowledgements*
*The author would like to thank The Vincent Wildlife Trust for long-standing support for his work on pine martens.*

# Polecat

***Figure 8.1.*** **Polecat in winter pelage.**
[Frank Greenaway/The Vincent Wildlife Trust].

# 8. Polecat

*By Johnny Birks*

## 8.1. Background Biology

Much of the information in this section is taken from summaries in Birks & Kitchener (1999) and Birks & Kitchener (2008).

The polecat *Mustela putorius* (**Fig. 8.1**) is a medium-sized member of the weasel family, with the typical elongated mustelid body shape and short legs. Males are considerably larger (typically 1400 g in weight and measuring 59 cm total length) than females (790 g and 50 cm). The polecat has a two-tone body fur colour that is most obvious in winter pelage, when the soft, pale yellow underfur is long and thick beneath the glossy black guard hairs, giving the animal a 'black and tan' appearance.

The most distinctive pelage feature is the striking 'bandit mask' pattern of light and dark fur on the animal's face (**Figs. 8.1** and **8.2**); this helps to distinguish the polecat from the feral mink *Neovison vison*, which is similar in size and shape but lacks pale facial fur above its white chin patch. Known colour mutations include albino and erythristic forms (**Fig. 8.2**). The presence of feral or escaped ferrets, which are interfertile with wild polecats, also creates identification and recording difficulties, especially where introgressive hybrids are present in the wild (**Fig. 8.2**). These animals tend to be paler in colour than true polecats, but their field signs are identical to those of true polecats. Ferrets apparently pose no threat to the genetic integrity of the true polecat in Britain, and evidence that the true polecat is the 'winner' in any competition between the two forms (Birks 2008), predicates the case for adopting a relaxed approach to distinguishing between them in surveys.

The polecat is a terrestrial generalist carnivore that preys on a wide range of mammals, birds and amphibians. Where wild rabbits *Oryctolagus cuniculus* are abundant these tend to dominate the polecat's diet; rabbit burrows are used by polecats for both foraging and resting purposes. In winter, polecats may prey upon concentrations of rodents around food stores in farmyards, leading to the risk of exposure to anti-coagulant rodenticides. Secondary rodenticide poisoning may affect as much as 50 % of the polecat population each winter, though the lethally affected proportion is not known (Shore *et al.* 2003).

Polecats are solitary animals (with the exception of family groups comprising mothers with kits), are strictly nocturnal (except for mid-summer when mother polecats and their kits may be active in daytime), and occupy a home range that includes year-round foraging resources and several resting sites. Home range size varies according to polecat gender and habitat quality, with males on lowland farmland typically occupying ranges of 212 ha and females 125 ha. Live-trapping studies suggest a mean winter population density of approximately one polecat per km$^2$. Communication between individuals is mainly by scent, though polecats do not apparently deposit scats (faeces) at prominent and accessible sites in the manner of some other carnivores; volatile, foul-smelling secretions from the anal glands are used in defence against predators.

Mating mainly occurs in March, followed by a gestation of 40–43 days. Females produce one litter per year, usually in May (litter size 5–10). Kits are typically born in a rabbit burrow; the young develop fast before dispersing in September to establish home ranges of their own. Eighty percent of polecats die in their first year; maximum lifespan is probably 4–5 years.

## 8.2. Habitat Requirements

Polecats are not strongly associated with any particular habitat type, though they tend to be less abundant in upland areas compared with the lowlands.

Provided there are adequate sources of uncontaminated prey and secure resting sites the polecat can maintain successful populations in a wide range of habitats including farmland, forest, riparian, coastal fringe (e.g. sand dunes) and suburbia (Birks & Kitchener 2008). In continental Europe, however, the polecat shows a greater association with wetlands and riparian habitats. This difference might be explained by the greater abundance of wild rabbits in Britain compared with continental Europe.

The rabbit is a key component of the polecat's diet in Britain and an important driver of its current population recovery and range expansion (Birks & Kitchener 1999). Where rabbits are present in reasonable numbers, polecats are able to feed and find daytime resting sites in rabbit burrows. Rabbit burrows may comprise 80 % of daytime resting sites used by polecats on lowland farmland, making the species vulnerable to rabbit control methods based upon the fumigation or destruction of burrows.

Polecats typically move around their home ranges by following linear habitat features such as field boundaries, streams and woodland edges; these provide some protection against predators as well as harbouring prey. Therefore, landscapes in which foraging areas are well-connected by linear features

*Figure 8.2.* **Polecat and polecat-ferrets.**
True polecat (upper left), conforming to phenotype with no evidence of ferret in pelage.  Erythristic polecats (upper right).  Polecat in summer pelage (middle left) and winter pelage (middle right).  'Dark' polecat-ferret which is superficially polecat-like, with subtle evidence of ferret in pelage (bottom left).  'Pale' polecat-ferret, with a pelage generally much too pale to be mistaken for a polecat (bottom right).
[Lynda Barton; Mr & Mrs Haworth; Nigel Beidas; Johnny Birks/The Vincent Wildlife Trust].

may be more attractive to polecats than those in which such areas are relatively isolated.

The polecat is commonly found living close to human habitation, often in rural areas where farmyards are occupied in association with predation upon commensal rodents (Birks 1998). However, there are many recent records of wild polecats from gardens, and many of these have come from the fringes of large urban areas such as Manchester; breeding has been reported beneath garden sheds and decking (Birks 2008).

Polecats appear especially vulnerable to road traffic casualties, perhaps because they forage for fresh carrion by roadsides. There is some evidence that they cannot establish and maintain successful populations where the density of busy roads is high.

Consequently, although polecats may occur in the urban fringe, extensive urban habitat and dense transport corridors may represent a population sink and a barrier to dispersal.

## 8.3. Status and Distribution

The polecat does not occur in the wild in Ireland, though some populations of feral ferrets are established there.

Following a devastating historical decline in Britain caused by excessive culling in the late 19th and early 20th centuries (Langley & Yalden 1977), the polecat is currently expanding its range (see *Fig. 8.3* for current distribution). From an early 1900s stronghold in upland mid-Wales, the polecat spread slowly in response to reduced

culling pressure to repopulate most of Wales and the western midlands of England by the end of the 20th century; informal reintroductions have restored the species to some other areas such as Cumbria, central southern England and parts of Scotland (Birks & Kitchener 1999). Recent national surveys have tracked the pattern of continuing spread in the 21st century, with the most active areas of current range expansion in the East Midlands and southern England (Birks 2008). The polecat's northward expansion from its main range in the English midlands appears to be constrained by the presence of dense urban areas, Pennine uplands and transport corridors between Liverpool and Doncaster. If this zone proves to be an impermeable barrier for polecat dispersal, the only viable route northward for an expanding midlands population lies to the east of Sheffield and Doncaster.

Our understanding of the polecat's status and distribution in Britain is complicated by the common occurrence of feral or escaped ferrets, a close congener that is regarded as a domesticated form of the wild polecat. Information from the latest (2004–2006) national polecat distribution survey (Birks 2008) was used to define three 'polecat purity zones' based upon the proportion of true polecats and polecat-ferrets among verifiable records from each vice-county. Perhaps predictably, the areas of lowest polecat purity (where < 85 % of records were true polecats) were found around the fringes of the polecat's expanding range and among the reintroduced populations in north-west England and Scotland. Encouragingly,

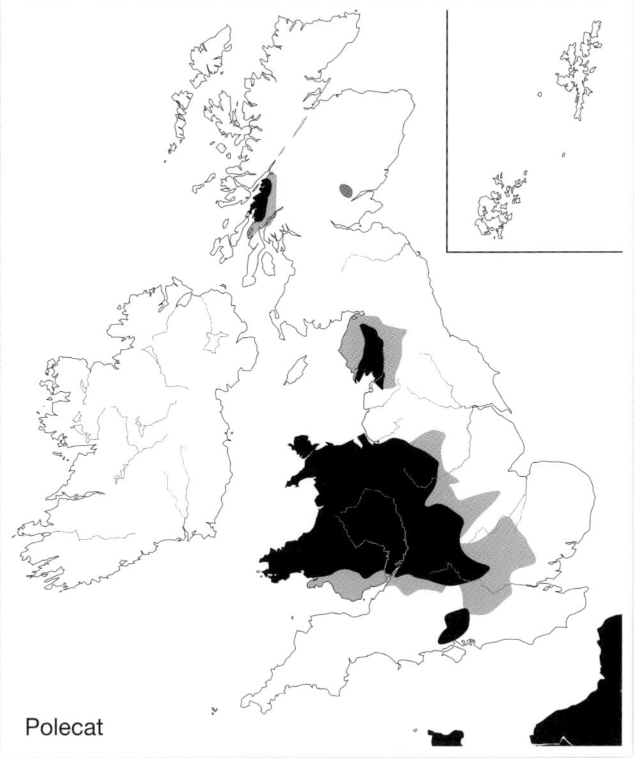

**Polecat**

*Figure 8.3.* **The distribution map of polecats for the British Isles.**
Black indicates regular or usual range; dark grey, scattered but regular occurrence; light grey, rare occurrences, vagrants, or scarce and beyond the regular range. Note that the polecat's range in England is expanding and, in Scotland, further small populations of uncertain origin and status may be established.
[from: Harris & Yalden (2008) *Mammals of the British Isles: Handbook,* 4th edition. Mammal Society; with minor amendments].

there is evidence to suggest that polecat-ferrets do not compete successfully with true polecats in the wild, so introgression with ferrets does not currently pose a significant threat to the genetic integrity of the polecat in Britain (Birks 2008).

## 8.4. Legislative Protection

The polecat is partly protected in England and Wales under the Wildlife and Countryside Act 1981 (Schedule 6) and the Conservation of Species and Habitats Regulations 2010 (Schedule 4). In Scotland, its listing on Schedule 3 of the Conservation (Natural Habitats, &c.) Regulations 1994 provides similar protection. This prohibits certain methods of taking or killing wild polecats. Licences are required in relation to trapping for research or survey purposes. Because the polecat is not listed on Schedule 5 of the Wildlife and Countryside Act 1981, it is not generally viewed as a 'protected species'.

The polecat also receives protection in Wales and England under the Natural Environment and Rural Communities Act (2006) requiring all public bodies to have regard for biodiversity conservation.

## 8.5. Summary of UK BAP Status and Recommended Actions

The polecat was listed in 2007 as a priority species for conservation in the UK BAP, and is on the Biodiversity Lists for England and Wales (listed as a Species of Principal Importance under the NERC Act, 2006).

The BAP recommended actions for the polecat are (http://www.jncc.gov.uk/_speciespages/2253.pdf):

- maintain and enhance field margin and wetland fringe habitats and their associated prey populations (especially wild rabbits *Oryctolagus cuniculus* and amphibians);

- monitor levels of exposure to rodenticides and assess lethal and sub-lethal effects upon populations;

- assess patterns of reproductive introgression with feral ferrets to identify threats to genetic integrity of polecat populations;

- clarify and publicise legal obligations facing trappers likely to kill or injure polecats in spring traps set for other species;

- raise public awareness of polecat identity (as distinct from ferret and mink) and promote sound husbandry as means to avoid conflicts with game- and poultry-keeping.

## 8.6. Survey Methodology

The type and extent of survey that is appropriate in each case will be dependent on the purposes of the survey. In some cases a survey may be designed to answer several questions, and a number of different survey types may be carried out at the same time. In the majority of cases it will be appropriate to collect information using a combination of desk study and field survey.

### *Establishing the presence of or absence of polecats*

Any attempt to establish the presence or absence of polecats on a site should be preceded by a desk study and data search to determine the status and distribution of the species in relation to the site. The desk study needs to take account of the polecat's currently expanding range in Britain, as well as the possibility that further unreported translocations may have restored the polecat to other parts of its former range. The VWT's latest polecat survey report (currently Birks 2008) should be consulted to establish whether the site lies within or close to a vice-county with an established population. More local evidence of polecat presence should be gathered via a request for recent records from the local Biological Records Centre and the VWT.[13]

If the site lies within or close to a vice-county with an established polecat presence, and if it supports non-isolated rural or suburban habitats in which favoured polecat prey such as wild rabbits, small rodents or amphibians are present, then it is prudent to assume that a polecat population is present. This assumption can reasonably be made because the polecat is a wide-ranging habitat generalist that occupies a variety of natural and human-modified environments, including the urban fringe. In Scotland, however, where the polecat is much less well-established than in Wales and England, and the species' status is not well understood, it is less safe to assume that a population is present within 'positive' vice-counties identified by the VWT in Birks (2008); in such cases more recent records should be sought from relevant sources to confirm status.

Another reason for making assumptions about polecat presence is because detecting the species at site level, though possible, is more time-consuming than for most other carnivores. Therefore, much expense may be saved by simply assuming polecat presence, unless there is a particular requirement to confirm presence or absence on a site.

A major constraint upon efforts to detect polecats on a site arises from the fact that, unlike some other carnivores, field signs of the species are neither readily found nor distinctive. Apart from depositing scats (faeces) at den sites (in latrines

---

[13] http://www.vwt.org.uk

that are typically inaccessible to a human search), polecats in Britain do not appear to mark prominent locations in their home ranges with scats (polecat scats are typically 50–70 mm long, 5–9 mm in diameter, cylindrical, twisted and tapered at one end). Even where field signs such as footprints or scats are found, the likely presence of feral ferrets means that it is not safe to infer polecat presence or absence on this evidence alone. Furthermore, the scats and footprints of feral American mink are very similar to those of polecats and feral ferrets, though mink footprints tend to be more splayed and star-shaped when compared with the more forward-pointing toes of polecat prints (Harrington *et al.* 2008) (polecat footprints are typically 30–40 mm long and 25–35 mm wide).

In view of the above constraints, efforts to confirm the presence or absence of polecats on a site must be based upon methods that allow visual inspection of specimens. This approach is constrained by the polecat's strictly nocturnal habits and its tendency to live at relatively low population densities with attendant low contact rates; nevertheless, live trapping has been used successfully to detect polecats at a range of sites using a standardised approach. Under current wildlife legislation, live trapping of polecats requires a licence from the appropriate SNCO.

The following standard approach to sampling polecats by live trapping (*Fig. 8.4*) was developed in the 1990s by the VWT (further details are available in Birks 1997; and Birks & Kitchener 1999):

- the trapping season should be October to March inclusive (the polecat population is relatively high and stable during this period, which avoids the breeding season and late summer juvenile dispersal period);

- traps should be single entry, treadle-operated weldmesh cage traps designed for catching mink, with approximate dimensions 76 x 15 x 15 cm;

- the sampling unit should be a 1 x 1 km square of the Ordnance Survey Grid (a monad); each monad is divided into 16 cells of 250 m x 250 m and a single cage trap should be placed in each cell at the most suitable location available, ideally in a linear feature such as a hedgerow (note that the distribution and density of traps may be varied from this standard approach in order to meet local survey requirements and site characteristics, but doing so would prevent the comparison of trapping results with data derived elsewhere using the standard approach);

- the 16 traps should be baited with fresh meat, covered in dry hay and concealed with other locally derived material; the dry hay provides shelter and gives trapped polecats something soft to pull at with their teeth;

- traps should be set for seven nights and checked every morning at daybreak and every evening at dusk; only traps with a closed door should be approached closely to identify the capture, trapped polecats tend to have pulled quantities of dry hay inside the trap so that they may be difficult to see;

- trapped polecats stay relatively calm if they are allowed to remain largely covered by hay or other material (e.g. a hessian sack can be used to cover the trap during processing); if a polecat feels threatened it may produce a sharp 'chack' noise and a powerful defensive stink; bearing this in mind, the polecat should be weighed in the trap (to allow an estimate of gender), examined, photographed and individually marked with coloured stock marker spray before being released from the trap;

- each trap that catches a polecat should be left closed for one night to reduce the risk of immediate recapture; fresh bait should be added to traps after each capture and, in the absence of captures, on the morning of the fourth trap check.

### Other potential detection techniques

Polecats and ferrets are too closely related, and their genes too intermixed following many decades of introgression, for the two forms to be distinguished by current molecular genetic techniques. However, there is potential to develop the use of camera traps for the detection of polecats in presence/absence surveys (*Fig. 8.5*). There is still research to be done to demonstrate that camera traps can detect polecats at low population densities, and that the photographs can consistently and reliably distinguish polecats from ferrets.

### Identifying features of particular significance

In relation to many projects it will be important to establish whether important habitat features, such as polecat foraging areas, linear dispersal routes/habitat links and potential resting sites are present within the area of the works. The extent and quality of such features will influence the probability that the site supports polecats. This assessment will require walkover surveys to identify and map any of the following features present on the site:

- concentrations of active rabbit burrows (used by polecats for foraging and resting);

- obvious concentrations of other potential prey (e.g. brown rat infestations or spawning amphibians);

*Figure 8.4.* **Live trapping a polecat.**
[Andy Cross; Johnny Birks].

*Figure 8.5.* **Wild polecat recorded at night by infra-red flash 'camera trap'.**
[David Oakley].

- rough tussocky grassland supporting small mammal populations (foraging);
- ponds and other wetlands, including streams and marshes (foraging and commuting);
- farm buildings, especially those harbouring commensal rodents close to stored grain or stock food (foraging) or stacks of hay or straw (used for resting);
- woodland, scrub and hedgerows (foraging, commuting and dispersal).

## 8.7. Impact Assessment, Mitigation, Compensation and Enhancement

### Habitat loss or loss of key features

It is important to assess the potential effects of projects upon polecats at an appropriate scale. Polecat populations are composed of individuals occupying contiguous or overlapping home ranges that are typically < 3 km² in size. Mean winter population densities on lowland farmland where the species is well established approximate to one polecat per km², so most developments will inevitably affect only a small number of resident individuals. Taking account of the species' low population density, the following is a guide to the likely level of impact upon polecat populations associated with developments of different scales: small-scale developments (e.g. construction of < 5 new dwelling houses) will have insignificant impacts, especially if hedgerows and similar landscape features are retained; larger developments covering < 1 km² are likely to have a relatively low impact on local polecat populations because of the small number of individuals affected; more extensive developments (e.g. 'ecotowns' on greenfield sites) may have significant impacts at a Local or even Regional scale, with the scale of such impacts related to the loss of key resources, impeded polecat access to those resources, and the effect these have upon home range viability. The viability of a polecat home range depends upon an individual having safe access to many well-separated features within it, such as foraging areas and resting sites; some foraging areas may be important only in certain seasons, nevertheless their accessible presence may be crucial to long-term home range viability. So, even relatively small-scale development projects may involve the loss of important habitat features that could significantly reduce the viability of one or more polecat home ranges. The significance of any such losses will need to be determined on a case-by-case basis.

Any significant habitat losses, such as foraging areas and commuting routes, will need to be mitigated through creation of replacement features with the same characteristics.

Losses of other key features will need to be mitigated through habitat creation. All development schemes should be aiming to deliver biodiversity enhancements; the provision of features of potential value to polecats can be achieved through the creation of new woodland, scrub, rough grassland, ponds and other wetlands. An important design consideration in the maintenance of viable polecat home ranges is the retention of connectivity between retained or newly created habitats and any adjacent rural areas.

### Habitat fragmentation

The breaching or removal of linear habitat features such as hedgerows and other field boundaries could affect polecat home range viability. This is especially likely in the case of highway schemes, where a well-used commuting or dispersal route breached by a new barrier would, in the absence of mitigation, carry a high risk of mortality through road traffic accidents.

In order to reduce the effects of habitat fragmentation upon polecat home range viability, the following principles should be followed wherever possible as part of the design process:

- retain important areas of foraging habitat, and links between these, as part of development layouts;
- where separation of foraging areas is unavoidable, establish alternative 'safe' commuting routes that do not carry elevated risks of mortality (e.g. raised ledges beside watercourses under wide culverts).

These design principles will serve to reduce fragmentation effects and reduce the potential for mortality of animals (see below).

### Mortality of animals

Direct impacts during the ground clearance or construction phase could arise through the destruction of daytime resting sites (e.g. rabbit burrows) occupied by polecats, with the attendant risk of injury or mortality. This type of impact can be avoided simply by manual clearance of vegetation a day before any earth-moving work, so as to encourage any polecats to vacate resting sites in response to disturbance. Such clearance work should be undertaken outside the species' breeding season, which spans April–July.

Much greater mortality impacts may arise in the long term through the construction of highways that carry high traffic volumes at night when polecats are active. Road traffic accidents (RTAs) are a major cause of polecat mortality in Britain (Birks & Kitchener 1999), perhaps partly as a consequence of the species foraging at night for fresh carrion on roads. There is some evidence that polecat RTAs are concentrated in areas where rabbits are abundant close to roads

(Barrientos & Bolonio 2008).

New road schemes should incorporate ways of reducing polecat RTA mortality as part of their design. Such measures are likely to include the construction of road crossings of watercourses using wide span structures, such as viaducts, to allow movement of animals below the road. Where this is not possible, the provision of ledges within culverts or separate dry pipes can also be considered as safe commuting routes for polecats. 'Mortality hotspots' on existing road schemes may also need safe crossings for polecats to be 'retro-fitted'.

### Disturbance

Polecats are generally tolerant of human disturbance, often choosing to live and breed where disturbance levels are high. It is not an offence to disturb a polecat, even at its resting site.

## 8.8. Research Requirements

Key research requirements include:

- identification of habitat features associated with polecat RTA mortality hotspots in Britain; can we predict RTA hotspots and mitigate accordingly?

- develop the use of camera traps for detecting polecats; can they reveal phenotype clearly; can a camera trap protocol be developed and tested for effective site surveys?

- what mitigation options are available for reducing the impacts of roads on polecat mortality and habitat fragmentation?

  - do polecats use culverts beneath roads?

  - what is the effect of 'new style' vertical concrete barriers (VCBs) in central reservations on polecat movements?

  - how can linear features passing beneath large roads be modified to promote safe passage by polecats?

  - what design of fencing might be effective at keeping polecats off roads and guiding them towards safe crossings?

## 8.9. References and Bibliography

Barrientos, R. & Bolonio, L. (2008) The presence of rabbits adjacent to roads increases polecat road mortality. *Biodiversity Conservation* DOI 10.1007/s10531-008-9499-9

Birks, J. D. S. (1997) A volunteer-based system for sampling variations in the abundance of polecats (*Mustela putorius*). *Journal of Zoology* **243**: 857–863.

Birks J. D. S. (1998) Secondary rodenticide poisoning risk arising from winter farmyard use by the European polecat *Mustela putorius*. *Biological Conservation* **85**: 233–240.

Birks J. D. S. & Kitchener, A.C. (1999) *The distribution and status of the polecat* Mustela putorius *in Britain in the 1990s*. The Vincent Wildlife Trust.

Birks, J. D. S. (2008) *The Polecat Survey of Britain 2004-2006: a report on the polecat's distribution, status and conservation*. The Vincent Wildlife Trust.

Birks, J. (2009) The polecat in Britain – continuing recovery. *British Wildlife* **20**: 237–244.

Birks, J. D. S. & Kitchener, A. C. (2008) Polecat. In: Harris, S. & Yalden, D. W. (eds) *Mammals of the British Isles: Handbook,* 4th edition, pp. 476–485. The Mammal Society.

Harrington, L. A., Harrington, A. L., & Macdonald, D.W. (2008) Distinguishing tracks of mink *Mustela vison* and polecat *Mustela putorius*. *European Journal of Wildlife Research* **54**: 367–371.

Langley, P. J. W. & Yalden, D. W. (1977) The decline of the rarer carnivores in Great Britain during the nineteenth century. *Mammal Review* **7**: 95–116.

Shore, R. F., Birks, J. D. S., Afsar, A., Wienburg, C. L. & Kitchener, A. C. (2003) Spatial and temporal analysis of second-generation anticoagulant rodenticide residues in polecats (*Mustela putorius*) from throughout their range in Britain, 1992–1999. *Environmental Pollution* **122**:183–193.

### Acknowledgements

*The author would like to thank The Vincent Wildlife Trust for long-standing support for his work on polecats.*

***Figure 9.1.*** Dormouse, water vole, greater horseshoe bat and otter. [Pat Morris; Cresswell].

## 9. A Literature Review for Other UK BAP Mammals
*By the editors*

*As discussed in the Introduction, several UK BAP mammals (notably the hazel dormouse, water vole, several bat species and otter) have comprehensive guidelines for their conservation, and so have not been considered in detail in this publication. Below is a brief summary of existing sources of relevant information for these species.*

### 9.1. Hazel Dormouse

Bright, P. W, Mitchell, P. & Morris, P. A. (1994) Dormouse distribution: survey techniques, insular ecology and selection of sites for conservation. *Journal of Applied Ecology* **31**: 329–339.

Bright, P. W. & Morris, P. (2008) Hazel dormouse *Muscardinus avellanarius*. In: Harris, S. & Yalden, D. W. (eds) *Mammals of the British Isles: Handbook,* 4th edition, pp 76–81. The Mammal Society, Southampton.

Bright, P. W., Morris, P. & Mitchell-Jones, T. (2006) *The Dormouse Conservation Handbook,* 2nd Edition. English Nature.

Chanin, P. & Gubert, L. (2011) Surveying hazel dormice (*Muscardinus avellanarius*) with tubes and boxes: a comparison. *Mammal Notes* **4**: 1–16.

Dormouse Species Action Plan: http://www.ukbap. org.uk/UKPlans.aspx?ID=462 (original UK BAP information) and http://ukbars.defra.gov.uk/plans/ national_plan.asp?SAP=%7B433CF30C%2DA 92C%2D487D%2DA1BE%2D8BD7D0D17218} (current information).

Highways Agency (2001) *Design Manual for Roads and Bridges, Volume 10, Section 4, Part 5. Nature Conservation Advice in Relation to Dormice.* HA 97/01. The Stationery Office, London. http://www. dft.gov.uk/ha/standards/dmrb/vol10/section4/ ha9701.pdf

IEEM (2011) *Technical Guidance Series. Competencies for Species Survey: Hazel Dormouse.* IEEM. http://www.ieem.net/docs/ CSS%20-%20HAZEL%20DORMOUSE%20 (31.8.2011).pdf

Juskaitis, R. (2008) *The Common Dormouse Muscardinus avellanarius: Ecology, Population Structure and Dynamics.* Institute of Ecology of Vilnius University Publishers, Vilnius.

Morris, P. (2011) *Dormice.* 2nd edition. British Natural History Series, Whittet Books.

Wouters, A., Cresswell, W., Wells, D., Downs, N. & Dean, M. (2010) Dormouse mitigation and translocation. *The Dormouse Monitor,* **Autumn 2010**: 3.

### 9.2. Water Vole

Capreolus Wildlife Consultancy (2005) *The ecology and conservation of water voles in upland habitats.* Scottish Natural Heritage Commissioned Report No. 099 (ROAME No. F99AC320).

Dean, M. (2003) Development mitigation for water voles: a research project into the effectiveness of 'displacement' as a mitigation technique. *In Practice* **39**: 10–14.

IEEM (2011) *Technical Guidance Series. Competencies for Species Survey: Water Vole.* IEEM. http://www.ieem.net/docs/CSS%20-%20 WATER%20VOLE%20%2831.8.2011%29.pdf

Morris, P. A., Morris, M. J., MacPherson, D., Jefferies, D. J., Strachan, R. & Woodroffe, G. L. (1998) Estimating numbers of the water vole, *Arvicola terrestris* – a correction to the published method. *Journal of Zoology, London* **246**: 61–62.

Natural England (2008) *Water Voles – the law in practice: guidance for planners and developers.* Natural England, Peterborough.

Natural England (2011) *Water voles and development: licensing policy.* Technical Information Note TIN042 (2nd edition). Natural England, Peterborough.

Raynor, R. (2005) *Conserving Scotland's Water Voles.* SNH. http://www.snh.org.uk/publications/ on-line/wildlife/voles/default.asp

Strachan, R. & Moorhouse, T. (2011) *Water Vole Conservation Handbook,* 3rd edition. Wildlife Conservation Research Unit, Oxford.

Water Vole Species Action Plan: http://www.ukbap. org.uk/UKPlans.aspx?ID=115 (original UK BAP information) and http://ukbars.defra.gov.uk/plans/ national_plan.asp?SAP=%7B426A6AE6%2DA969 %2D4305%2DB859%2DDF92B02814B3} (current information).

Woodroffe, G. L., Lambin, X. & Strachan R. (2008) Water vole *Arvicola terrestris* In: Harris, S. & Yalden, D. W. (eds) *Mammals of the British Isles: Handbook,* 4th edition, pp 110–117. The Mammal Society, Southampton.

### 9.3. Bats

Hundt, L. (2012) *Bat Surveys – Good Practice Guidelines,* 2nd edition. Bat Conservation Trust, London.

Miller, H. (2012) *Professional Training Standards for Ecological Consultants.* Bat Conservation Trust, London.

Highways Agency (1999) *Design Manual for Roads and Bridges, Volume 10, Section 4, Part 5. Nature Conservation Advice in Relation to Bats.* HA 80/99.

The Stationery Office, London. http://www.dft.gov.uk/ha/standards/dmrb/vol10/section4/ha8099.pdf

Highways Agency (2008) *Nature conservation in relation to bats*. Interim Advice Note 116/08. http://www.dft.gov.uk/ha/standards/ians/pdfs/ian116.pdf

Highways Agency (2011) *A Review of Bat Mitigation in Relation to Highway Severance*. The Stationery Office, London. http://www.highways.gov.uk/knowledge_compendium/assets/documents/Portfolio/A_Review_of_Bat_Mitigation_in_Relation_to_Highway_Severance_PIN_515368.doc.pdf

IEEM (2011) Technical Guidance Series. *Competencies for Species Survey: Bats*. IEEM. http://www.ieem.net/docs/CSS%20-%20BATS%20%20(31.8.2011).pdf

Racey, P. A. (2008) Bats: Order Chiroptera, In: Harris, S. & Yalden, D. W. (eds) *Mammals of the British Isles: Handbook*, 4th edition, pp 292–297. The Mammal Society, Southampton.

Mitchell-Jones, A. J. (2004) *Bat Mitigation Guidelines*. English Nature, Peterborough.

Mitchell-Jones, A. J. & McLeish, A. P. (2004) *Bat Workers' Manual*. Joint Nature Conservation Committee, Peterborough.

Schofield, H. W. (2008) *The Lesser Horseshoe Bat Conservation Handbook*. The Vincent Wildlife Trust.

Stebbings, R., Mansfield, H. & Fasham, M. (2005) Bats. In: Hill, D., Fasham, M., Tucker, P., Shewry M. & Shaw P (eds) *Handbook of Biodiversity Methods: Survey, Evaluation and Monitoring*, pp 433–449. Cambridge University Press, Cambridge.

Williams, C. (2010) *Biodiversity for Low and Zero Carbon Buildings: A Technical Guide for New Build*. RIBA Publishing.

See also the Bat Conservation Trusts website for further publications on Professional Guidance and Good Practice: http://www.bats.org.uk/pages/guidanceforprofessionals.html

Various Bat Species Action Plans: http://www.ukbap.org.uk/SpeciesGroup.aspx?ID=19 (original UK BAP information) and http://ukbars.defra.gov.uk/plans/national.asp (search for specific bats for current information).

## 9.4. Otter

Chanin, P. (2003a) *Ecology of the European Otter*. Conserving Natura 2000 Rivers: Ecology Series No. 10. English Nature, Peterborough.

Chanin, P. (2003b) *Monitoring the Otter*. Conserving Natura 2000 Rivers: Monitoring Series No. 10. English Nature, Peterborough.

Chanin, P. (2005) *Otter surveillance in SACs: testing the protocol*. English Nature Research Report No. 664.

Crawford, A. K. (2010) *The fifth otter survey of England 2009–10*. Environment Agency, Bristol.

Grogan, A., Philcox, C. & Macdonald, D. (2001) *Nature Conservation and Roads: Advice in Relation to Otters*. Wildlife Research Conservation Unit, Oxford.

Highways Agency (2001) *Design Manual for Roads and Bridges, Volume 10, Section 4, Part 5. Nature Conservation Advice in Relation to Otters*. HA 81/99. The Stationery Office, London. http://www.dft.gov.uk/ha/standards/dmrb/vol10/section4/ha8199.pdf

Jefferies, D. J. & Woodroffe, G. L. (2008) Otter *Lutra lutra*, In: Harris, S. & Yalden, D. W. (eds) *Mammals of the British Isles: Handbook*, 4th edition, pp 437–447 The Mammal Society, Southampton.

Jones, T. & Jones, D. (2004) *Otter Survey of Wales 2002*. Environment Agency Wales.

Kruuk, H. (1995) *Wild Otters: Predation and Populations*. Oxford University Press, Oxford.

Kruuk, H. & Conroy, J. W. H. (1987) Surveying otter *Lutra lutra* populations: a discussion of problems with spraints. *Biological Conservation* **41**: 179–183.

Kruuk, H. (2006) *Otters: Ecology, Behaviour and Conservation*. Oxford University Press, USA.

Liles, G. (2003) *Otter Breeding Sites. Conservation and Management*. Conserving Natura 2000 Rivers: Conservation Techniques Series No. 5. English Nature, Peterborough.

MacPherson, D., MacPherson, J. L. & Morris, P. (2011) Rural roads as barriers to the movement of small mammals. *Applied Ecology and Environmental Research* **9**: 167–180.

Madsen, A. B. (1996) Otter *Lutra lutra* mortality in relation to traffic, and experience with newly established fauna passages at existing road bridges. *Lutra* **39**: 76–88.

Natural England (2008) Otter surveys – when do I need a licence? WML-G02 (02/11) http://www.naturalengland.org.uk/Images/wmlg02_tcm6-3750.pdf

Otter Species Action Plan: http://www.ukbap.org.uk/UKPlans.aspx?ID=428 (original UK BAP information) and http://ukbars.defra.gov.uk/plans/national_plan.asp?SAP=%7B8902DFBF%2D7932%2D47AF%2D9DD6%2DB7E4EAFC8863} (current information)

Strachan, R. (2007) *National survey of otter* Lutra lutra *distribution in Scotland 2003–04*. Scottish Natural Heritage Commissioned Report No. 211. http://www.snh.org.uk/pdfs/publications/commissioned_reports/Report%20No211.pdf

Strachan, R. (2011) *Otter Survey of Wales 2009–10: Technical Summary*. Environment Agency Wales, Cardiff.

Woodroffe, G. L. (1994) *The Otter*. The Mammal Society, London.

## Notes